C000147347

0100 10929591

Published in the UK in 2023
by Icon Books Ltd, Omnibus Business Centre,
39–41 North Road, London N7 9DP
info@iconbooks.com
www.iconbooks.com

Sold in the UK, Europe and Asia by
Faber & Faber Ltd, Bloomsbury House,
74–77 Great Russell Street,
London WC1B 3DA or their agents

Distributed in the UK, Europe and Asia
by Grantham Book Services, Trent Road,
Grantham NG31 7XQ

Distributed in Australia and New Zealand
by Allen & Unwin Pty Ltd, PO Box 8500,
83 Alexander Street, Crows Nest, NSW 2065

Distributed in South Africa
by Jonathan Ball, Office B4, The District,
41 Sir Lowry Road, Woodstock 7925

Distributed in India by Penguin Books India,
7th Floor, Infinity Tower-C, DLF Cyber City,
Gurgaon 122002, Haryana

Copyright © UniPress Books Ltd 2023

All rights reserved. No part of this book
maybe reproduced, transmitted or stored in
an information retrieval system in any form or by
any means, graphic, electronic or mechanical,
including photocopying, taping and recording,
without prior written permission from
the publisher.

Publisher: Jason Hook
Art director: Alexandre Coco
Commissioning editor: Kate Duffy
Illustrator: Robert Brandt

ISBN: 978-1-78578-941-0

Printed in China

1 2 3 4 5 6 7 8 9 10

| SHROPSHIRE LIBRARIES | |
| --- | --- |
| 0100 10929591 | |
| Askews & Holts | 30-Jan-2023 |
| 500 | £14.99 |
| SL | |

# SCIENCE

Consultant Editor
**MARK PEPLOW**

ICON BOOKS

# INTRODUC

**S**cience constitutes a colossal territory of human knowledge. Centuries ago, it was just about possible for a scholar to know their way around every region of science. But as the pace of discovery has quickened, the frontiers of science have expanded at an astonishing rate. So how are we to make sense of today's sprawling scientific landscape?

We need a map. The short cuts in this book will guide you on a journey through science, from the dawn of time to the very latest discoveries in gene editing and quantum computing. Along the way we'll meet some of the key characters behind these discoveries, who show that science is not just a collection of facts – but a deeply human enterprise: a flawed but vibrant process for figuring out how the universe works.

Our expedition starts with a series of origin stories: the Big Bang, our Earth's history and the evolution of life. Then we'll see how energy and forces mould the cosmos, and meet the minuscule atoms and molecules that make up the everyday matter around us. This path leads us ever deeper into the strange subatomic world of quantum physics. Down here, we can measure our steps in quadrillionths of a quintillionth of a centimetre, where a

# TION

new theory of quantum gravity might be found at the very edge of our understanding.

After that, we'll come up for air and navigate the mechanics of life, from cells and photosynthesis to genes and enzymes. Our knowledge of what makes life tick has helped researchers to develop vaccines, antibiotics and other medicines that have dramatically extended our lifespans over the past century. It has also led to new technologies, such as cell reprogramming, which promise to continue these amazing advances in the science of healthcare.

Zooming out even further reveals how the Earth supports life and how we might sustain our environment for generations to come. Then it's onwards to the stars, where countless worlds could host other intelligent civilisations. Our final destination is information itself – the lifeblood of science and the driving force behind the ongoing revolution in computing.

The terrain covered by this book offers a brief glimpse of the scientific world and leaves plenty more to explore. For now, we're glad you're joining us on this whistle-stop tour around 50 of the biggest ideas in science. We hope you enjoy the ride.

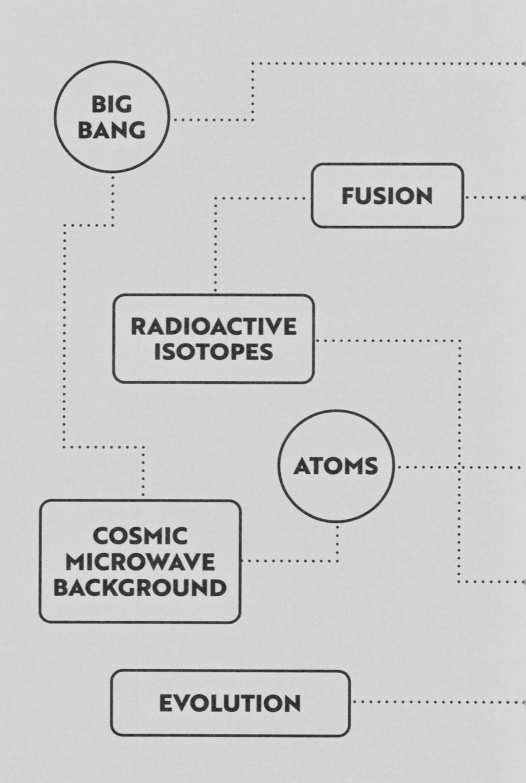

# CHAPTER 1

# ORIGINS

STARS

ELEMENTS

PRIMORDIAL EARTH

PLATE TECTONICS

# INTRODUCTION

How did we get here? Humans have mulled this existential question for millennia and science can provide us with some amazing answers. This chapter is all about origins, and what science tells us about the birth of the universe, the emergence of life and its evolution into the panoply of **SPECIES** on our planet today – including ourselves.

The quest to understand how we got here takes us on an epic journey across time and space. It all began 13.8 billion years ago, with an event called the **BIG BANG** that unleashed all the matter and energy in the universe from a single point (see page 14).

As the universe expanded, high-energy radiation from its earliest years was stretched out to longer wavelengths. Today, we see that radiation as **MICROWAVES** coming from every part of the cosmos. Known as the **COSMIC MICROWAVE BACKGROUND**, this residual echo from the Big Bang has left an enduring message from creation across the sky.

A few hundred thousand years after the Big Bang, the fiery plasma that filled the universe cooled down enough to form neutral atoms – hydrogen, helium and a bit of lithium. But the rest of the elements didn't start to appear until clumps of gas gradually coalesced to form the first stars hundreds of millions of years later.

**STARS** run on fusion power, crushing the nuclei of hydrogen atoms together to make helium, followed by carbon, oxygen and other elements. Really massive stars can build even heavier elements, before disgorging them in a spectacular **SUPERNOVA** explosion. Most of the elements in our bodies were formed by **FUSION** reactions inside stars (see page 16).

The swirling cloud of dust and gas that spawned our Sun also created our solar system's colourful array of planets. By studying radioactive isotopes from Earth's oldest rocks, scientists have figured out that our home world formed roughly 4.5 billion years ago (see page 18).

Since then, the Earth has undergone some spectacular changes. The slow churning of semi-molten rock beneath the planet's crust has shifted and reshaped the continents many times in a process called **PLATE TECTONICS** that helps to enrich the oceans with elements essential to life (see page 20).

There's still plenty of debate about how life first arose. One famous experiment attempted to mimic the conditions of the primordial Earth and found that sparking electricity through a heated mixture of water and various gases produced many of the basic building blocks of biological molecules (see page 22).

It's still a mystery how these molecules organised themselves into the single-celled organisms that ruled the Earth for billions of years. But it's clear that **EVOLUTION** gradually shaped them into more complex organisms that diversified into many different species (see page 24). Roughly 300,000 years ago, this process created a particularly brainy primate called *Homo sapiens* – the first modern human.

# ORIGINS MAP

## COSMOLOGY

### BIG BANG
Widely accepted theory for the birth of the universe around 13.8 billion years ago, in which it inflated from an infinitely dense single point.

### COSMIC MICROWAVE BACKGROUND
Leftover radiation from the early stage of the creation of the universe when it rapidly inflated and cooled. Used as evidence for the Big Bang.

### STAR
Massive astronomical object consisting of very hot gas called plasma in which hydrogen and helium fuse to form heavier elements, emitting energy in the form of light and heat.

### FUSION
When two atomic nuclei merge together to make a heavier one. Any difference in mass is due to the release or absorption of energy.

### GALAXY
A group of stars, clouds of gas, dust and other objects held together by gravity. There are probably billions of galaxies in the universe.

### SUPERNOVA
Powerful, visible explosion of a star at the end of its life that emits huge amounts of matter and energy.

## EVOLUTION

### CHARLES DARWIN
English naturalist, geologist and biologist (1809–82) who is credited with the theory that evolution occurs through a process of natural selection.

### NATURAL SELECTION
Evolutionary process in which organisms that are better suited to their environment are more likely to survive and pass advantageous traits on to their offspring.

### SPECIES
A group of organisms that can reproduce naturally with one another and create fertile offspring. When populations evolve to become new, distinct species, it is called speciation.

# PHYSICS

**MICROWAVES**

A type of electromagnetic radiation. Definitions vary, but may include wavelengths from one metre to one millimetre (frequencies of 300 MHz to 300 GHz) or 0.3 metre to three millimetres (one to 100 GHz).

**ELECTROMAGNETIC RADIATION**

Energy that propagates as electromagnetic waves travelling at the speed of light; includes radio waves, microwaves, infrared, visible light, ultraviolet, X-rays and gamma rays.

**RADIOACTIVE DECAY**

Process by which unstable atomic nuclei spontaneously emit particles and energy, and change into different, more stable nuclei.

**HALF-LIFE**

Time required for a quantity to reduce to half its initial value. In radioactive decay it is how long it takes half the nuclei in a sample to change.

**PLATE TECTONICS**

Theory that the Earth's solid outer crust is divided into large pieces ('plates') that move relative to each other, resulting in mountain ranges, volcanoes and earthquakes.

**EVOLUTION**

Biological theory that living things on Earth gradually change over time due to modifications in successive generations.

**ABIOGENESIS**

Theory of the chemical process by which the first simple forms of life emerged on Earth from non-living matter.

**RIBONUCLEIC ACID (RNA)**

Present in all living cells, a single-stranded molecule that contains information copied from DNA. Many forms of RNA have a role in making proteins.

**PRIMORDIAL SOUP**

Mixture of organic chemicals that could produce the basic building blocks of life when exposed to the right atmospheric conditions.

# Can we still hear the Big Bang?

**⟶ Yes, we can. It's known as cosmic microwave background radiation and it helps us to piece together the history of our universe. All we need to hear it is a radio receiver.**

Our universe was born in the Big Bang around 13.8 billion years ago. When we look into space, we can see galaxies other than our own moving away from us. We can tell galaxies are speeding away from us by their colour. Think of how an ambulance siren changes to a different pitch after it passes us, because as it moves away its sound waves stretch out. The same thing happens to light waves coming from galaxies. The waves are stretched and appear redder. As the galaxy moves faster, the redder its light becomes. This is known as red shift.

Red shift reveals that our universe is expanding, meaning that in the past it must have been much smaller. If we go back far enough, there was an instant when all the matter in the universe was packed into a single point that began to expand outwards – the Big Bang.

Following the Big Bang, the universe was flooded with radiation in the form of light. The young, super-hot universe inflated rapidly, then slowly cooled and, as it expanded, the light was stretched into microwaves. Now, all these billions of years later, there is still residual heat from the Big Bang in the form of leftover radiation, which can be detected by specialist microwave telescopes as a 'glow' pervading the whole sky. This glow is the cosmic microwave background (CMB), an echo of the Big Bang.

The CMB can't be seen by the naked eye because it is so cold – a mere 2.725°C above absolute zero (−273.15°C) – but we can hear it. American cosmologist Ralph Apher first predicted the CMB in 1948. However, it was later discovered accidentally in 1964 by Arno Penzias and Robert Wilson, who would go on to win the Nobel Prize in Physics. The astronomers were using a radio antenna to measure signals from space and were puzzled by the noise it was detecting. They thought it was some form of interference, but then realised the noise came uniformly from all over the sky, no matter what direction they pointed the antenna. They had detected the CMB.

Spotting the CMB was like discovering the ash from a long-since extinguished inferno. But it ensured the Big Bang – one of various hypotheses for the formation of the universe – became the theory of choice among cosmologists.

# COSMIC MICROWAVE BACKGROUND

It's rare that cosmology makes the front page of newspapers. But in 1992, when data from NASA's Cosmic Background Explorer (COBE) mission produced a map of the CMB, it was big news. The map is oval shaped to make presentation of the information simpler. It shows us that although CMB is present throughout the universe, there are very fine fluctuations within it – these are marked by different shades on the image, with the darker regions revealing where galaxies and other structures are being formed. These fluctuations help us more accurately determine the age and composition of the universe, including when the first stars were born.

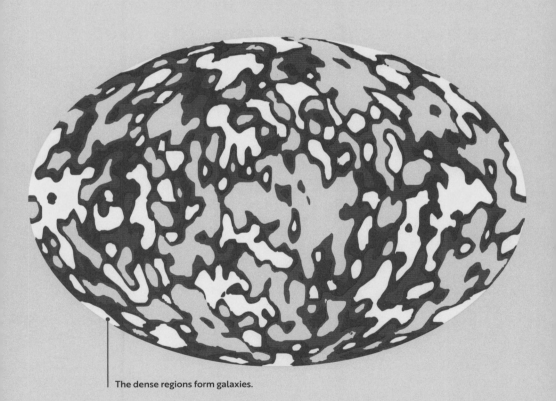

The dense regions form galaxies.

# How many stars does it take to make a human?

⟶ **Several, probably. Our own star, the Sun, sustains life on Earth. But most of the chemical elements in our bodies were made inside other stars that lived and died billions of years ago.**

Our bodies consist of a wonderful array of elements. About 99 per cent of our mass comes from just six chemical elements: oxygen, carbon, hydrogen, nitrogen, calcium and phosphorus. In addition, there are around twenty more elements inside us that are essential for life, including chlorine, magnesium and potassium.

Each of our hydrogen atoms has a proton in its nucleus that formed within one second of the Big Bang (see page 14). But most of the elements in our bodies were generated inside stars.

The Sun and other stars generate their energy by performing a kind of cosmic alchemy, transforming lighter elements into heavier ones in a process called fusion. The enormous heat and pressure of a star's core crushes together protons to create the nucleus of a helium atom. This process was first proposed by British astronomer Arthur Eddington in 1920 and later elaborated on by other scientists.

However, it was Fred Hoyle in the 1940s and 1950s who outlined how other fusion processes could build up larger atomic nuclei. Once a star's hydrogen is used up it contracts, making its core hot enough to fuse helium nuclei into elements such as carbon and oxygen. Lighter stars tend to stop there, and become white dwarf stars. But heavier stars can continue through the periodic table (see page 54) to produce iron, cobalt and nickel. In some stars, other nuclear reactions force extra neutrons into these nuclei, building up even heavier elements.

Then things may take an explosive turn. Without the outward pressure of fusion, a massive star's core collapses, crushing the nuclei together to form a neutron star or even a black hole (see page 42). The resultant shockwave blasts off the star's outer layers in a supernova explosion, disgorging all its elements into the cosmos. Scientists think that collisions between neutron stars, and between white dwarfs, are also important sources of the elements heavier than iron.

Every time stars collide or explode, they have the potential to seed new life across the cosmos. This star 'vomit' may gradually coalesce into clouds that give birth to new stars and planets. Given the age of our galaxy, many of the atoms in our bodies may have already been through several of these stellar resurrections.

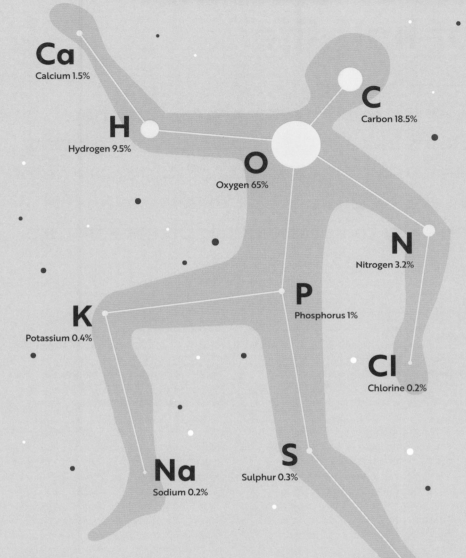

# STELLAR NUCLEOSYNTHESIS

**Ca**
Calcium 1.5%

**C**
Carbon 18.5%

**H**
Hydrogen 9.5%

**O**
Oxygen 65%

**N**
Nitrogen 3.2%

**K**
Potassium 0.4%

**P**
Phosphorus 1%

**Cl**
Chlorine 0.2%

**Na**
Sodium 0.2%

**S**
Sulphur 0.3%

**Mg**
Magnesium 0.1%

*Around two-thirds of the atoms in our bodies are hydrogen atoms almost as old as the universe itself. Even so, hydrogen only accounts for about 10 per cent of our mass because it is the lightest element. The rest of our atoms were created by nuclear fusion reactions in the hearts of stars. Oxygen and carbon are the most common of these, but even elements such as sulfur and magnesium, which make up less than 1 per cent of our mass are vital for life. As the astronomer Carl Sagan famously said: 'We're made of star stuff.'*

# What is the meaning of half-life?

**→ It's the time it takes for half the atoms in a sample of an element to decay. Measuring the products of this decay helps us estimate the age of rocks or artefacts, a vital key to unlocking our planet's history.**

All elements have half-lives because they all have radioactive isotopes. Eventually, their atomic nuclei break down in a process known as radioactive decay. An element's half-life is the time it takes for half the atoms in a given sample to do this. Highly radioactive elements, such as polonium and plutonium, have isotopes with very short half-lives. Stable elements, such as tin, can have isotopes with long half lives.

The nucleus of every atom of every chemical element contains protons and neutrons – except for hydrogen (see page 52). Although each atom of a given element has the same fixed number of protons in its nucleus, the number of neutrons can vary, leading to elements having different isotopes. While familiar elements such as oxygen have at least one stable isotope, their less stable isotopes decay more rapidly. Highly radioactive elements decay even faster, but the rate at which their isotopes decay varies.

Isotope half-lives range from billions of years to milliseconds. Additionally, atomic nuclei in a sample do not decay simultaneously – like bubbles in a bathtub they 'burst' sporadically until eventually they all break down.

The radiation emitted as some isotopes decay can be dangerous, such as that emitted by uranium used in nuclear power stations. Knowing its half-life lets us calculate how long to store radioactive waste until it's safe.

But radioactive decay has benefits too, allowing us to date rocks and fossils, or archaeological artefacts. By comparing the amount of an isotope in an object when it was created (or in a fossil when the animal or plant died) with the amount yet to undergo decay reveals how many half-lives have passed since it was created, and thereby its age.

The relatively unstable carbon-14 isotope is useful for dating archaeological objects a few thousand years old (the number 14 refers to the total number of protons and neutrons its nucleus contains). Potassium-40 is far more stable, decaying to argon-40 with a half-life of 1.25 billion years; comparing the amounts of both in ancient rocks helps determine the age of the Earth (roughly 4.5 billion years old) and its structures.

# RADIOMETRIC DATING

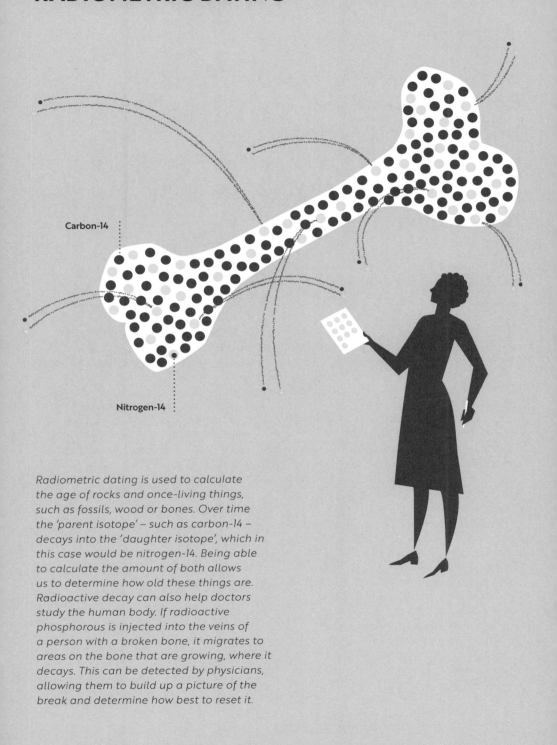

Carbon-14

Nitrogen-14

*Radiometric dating is used to calculate the age of rocks and once-living things, such as fossils, wood or bones. Over time the 'parent isotope' – such as carbon-14 – decays into the 'daughter isotope', which in this case would be nitrogen-14. Being able to calculate the amount of both allows us to determine how old these things are. Radioactive decay can also help doctors study the human body. If radioactive phosphorous is injected into the veins of a person with a broken bone, it migrates to areas on the bone that are growing, where it decays. This can be detected by physicians, allowing them to build up a picture of the break and determine how best to reset it.*

# Did the Earth move?

**→ Yes, it probably did, although it depends where you are on the planet because some regions move faster and more often than others. The Earth's crust is an ever-shifting jigsaw driven by forces beneath our feet.**

In 1912, geophysicist Alfred Wegener noted that the east coast of the Americas and the west coasts of Africa and Europe fitted together nicely. Had they drifted apart? Well, sort of. And while early theories of continental drift have been superseded, they spawned what we call plate tectonics.

The continents themselves don't drift, but the crust they sit on is being moved around by what lies beneath. At the Earth's centre is a dense iron-nickel core. At the surface is the crust. Between them is the mantle, a layer of hot, semi-solid rock accounting for two-thirds of our planet's mass.

Think of the mantle as a slowly boiling pot of water with convection currents continually bringing heated material to the surface. This cools, sinks and is replaced by new hot material. Floating atop these churning convection cells are the tectonic plates forming the Earth's crust. These convection cycles ensure the plates constantly shift.

Where tectonic plates converge (destructive plate boundaries), one is driven beneath the other. This creates a subduction zone, plunging into the mantle like a hot knife through butter. Volcanoes form as the melted plate rises back to the surface. Earthquakes in these areas are commonplace and may cause tsunamis. If plates collide in the ocean they form clefts, such as the Marianas Trench. If they collide where land masses meet, the crust crumples, pushing upwards to form mountain ranges such as the Himalayas.

Where plates diverge (constructive plate boundaries), a split appears in the crust. This is repeatedly filled by hot magma, healing the gap like a scab on a cut. The best example is the mid-Atlantic ridge pushing Europe and North America apart a few centimetres each year; Iceland is part of this ridge. Such plate boundaries appear on land too, with one example being Africa's Great Rift Valley.

Where plates neither converge nor diverge, they can slide alongside each other (transform fault boundaries). California's San Andreas Fault is one, alternately sticking and sliding, causing devastating earthquakes.

# PLATE TECTONICS

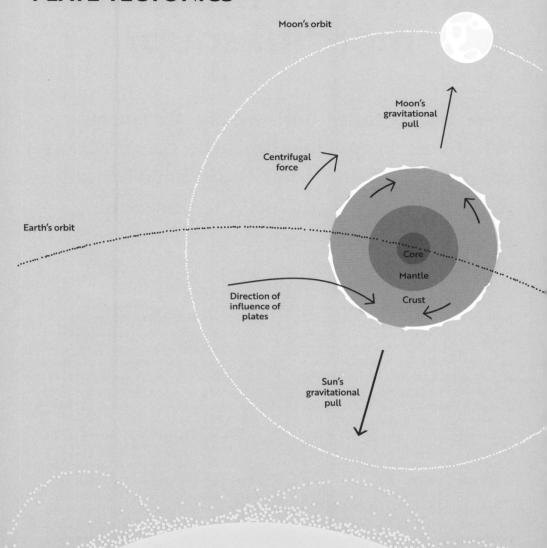

Moon's orbit

Moon's gravitational pull

Centrifugal force

Core

Mantle

Crust

Earth's orbit

Direction of influence of plates

Sun's gravitational pull

Recent research has suggested that in addition to convection in the Earth's mantle, the movement of tectonic plates may also be affected by the gravitational pulls of the Sun and Moon. In some instances, convection currents in the mantle don't seem strong enough to account for the tectonic activity seen on the Earth's surface. But if the mantle and the crust are also subject to the pull of the Sun and Moon, this may explain the actual levels of earthquake and volcanic activity we observe. In time, this new research may transform our understanding of what drives plate tectonics.

# Did life emerge from a primordial soup?

⟶ Yes, because here we are. But how? What was so special about the composition of that soup? And what could have turned its lifeless chemicals into the burgeoning biosphere that followed?

In 1953, at the University of Chicago in the US, Harold Urey and Stanley Miller set out to create the atmospheric conditions of early Earth.

Two weeks later, their interpretation of our planet's primordial soup had produced amino acids, the basic building blocks of proteins necessary for life. Subsequently, more sophisticated versions of the experiment yielded even more of the molecules, such as lipids, necessary for life to begin, such as lipids.

The rationale of the experiment was to show how undetermined chemical reactions in the soup could lead to the first living cell: a process called abiogenesis. This may have occurred more than once in our planet's history, but would be impossible now due to the current composition of Earth's atmosphere.

Numerous hypothetical routes to the appearance of that first living cell include the RNA world scenario, which suggests life began with a simple ribonucleic acid (RNA) molecule that could copy itself without help from other molecules. RNA, deoxyribonucleic acid (DNA, see page 94) and proteins are all central to life on Earth, but this hypothesis presumes that RNA proliferated first. RNA can drive chemical reactions such as proteins and carry genetic information such as DNA, which is why many palaeobiologists think life could have begun in an RNA world before proteins or DNA existed.

However, experiments have yet to demonstrate the theory in practice and alternative chemical paths to life have been proposed. One is panspermia, which is the bombardment of early Earth with meteorites carrying living organisms. Another is that life developed around warm, deep-ocean vents. The subject remains one of the most contentious in the field of life sciences.

Research into the development of early life has benefited greatly from studying other planets and moons in our solar system. For example, Saturn's moon Titan has an atmosphere containing complex organic molecules, offering a glimpse of conditions on early Earth.

# BUILDING BLOCKS OF LIFE

To recreate the concept of a primordial soup, researchers from the University of Chicago filled a glass bowl with water, hydrogen, ammonia and methane – what they considered matched the conditions on early Earth. They then heated it to mimic the warming of the Sun and passed electric sparks through it to simulate lightning. It was akin to putting the raw ingredients for a casserole into the oven and watching it transform as it cooked, although in this case the results would last very, very much longer.

# Is evolution a game of natural selection?

⟶ It really is. Natural selection is the process by which species evolve over time in response to environmental change. It is the driving force shaping life on Earth and remains one of the most successful theories ever.

In 1859, Charles Darwin published his book on his theory of evolution by natural selection amid a storm of controversy. He proposed that life was not created, but that it evolved. According to the theory, all living species are modified descendants of earlier species and all species share a common ancestor. In this way, all life forms are connected via an enormous tree of life.

He suggested that evolution is driven by natural selection or the 'survival of the fittest'. Members of the same species may be similar, but there are small, heritable differences that help certain individuals to survive. Some individuals, for example, may be better at evading predators or tolerating toxins. These individuals are said to be 'fitter' than those who lack such features and, as a result, they are more likely to reproduce and pass their winning characteristics on to the next generation. This leads to change over time, as beneficial characteristics become more common and harmful ones die out.

Over many generations and across time, these changes rack up, leading to speciation: the formation of new species. This usually occurs when different populations of the same species become so genetically different to each other that they can no longer produce offspring together. As more and more species form, life diversifies.

Sometimes, animals possess features with no obvious survival value. Peacocks, for example, have flashy, long tail feathers that would surely slow them down if they were being chased by a predator. The theory of natural selection predicts that this feature would disappear over time, yet it hasn't. Darwin had an explanation in the form of sexual selection, which is a special type of natural selection. Some features, he argued, persist over time because they make males more attractive to females, and therefore increase their likelihood of reproducing.

# EVOLUTION IN ACTION

*When the environment changes rapidly, the usually glacial rate of evolution speeds up. This happened during the Industrial Revolution, when a random genetic shift caused the peppered moth to change colour. The new dark-coloured version blended in well against the sooty-coated tree trunks where it rested during the day (top), while the older, lighter version stood out (bottom) and was more likely to be preyed upon. This led to change over time, as the darker form proliferated and the lighter form became less common.*

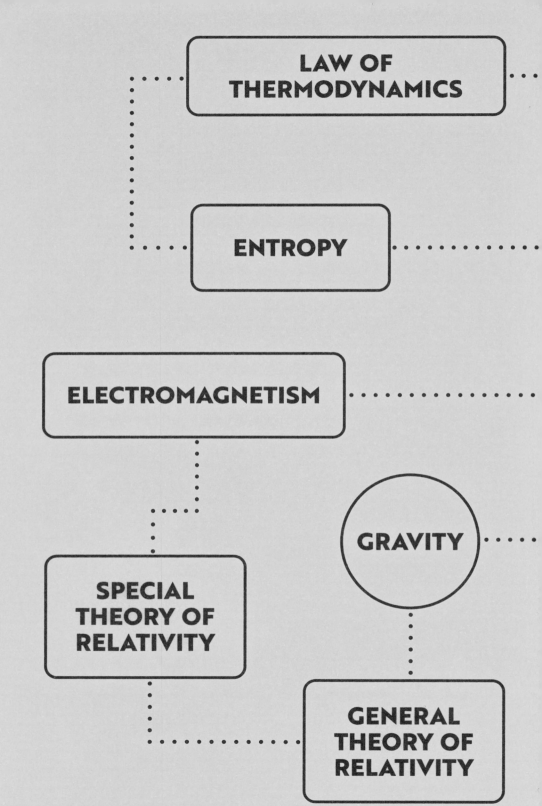

# CHAPTER 2

# ENERGY AND FORCES

LAWS OF MOTION

DARK MATTER

DARK ENERGY

# INTRODUCTION

**E**nergy and forces shape our universe. Our understanding of them allows us to explain why an apple falls from a tree and why the Sun shines – and it shows that the inner workings of the cosmos are both wondrous and deeply weird.

**ENERGY** comes in many different forms. It is found in the heat of a glowing ember, the spinning of a flywheel and the chemical bonds inside an explosive. Yet these are all aspects of the same vigorous essence, which can change from one form to another and potentially do something useful along the way – in other words, energy is simply the capacity to do work. Crucially, energy also cannot be created or destroyed, an idea enshrined in the first law of **THERMODYNAMICS** (see page 36).

**FORCES**, meanwhile, are responsible for pushing or pulling things. Different forces act at every conceivable scale, binding together the constituents of an atomic nucleus or the stars in a swirling galaxy.

**ISAAC NEWTON** paved the way for our understanding of forces with his three **LAWS OF MOTION** (see page 32). He also realised that everything in the universe exerts a gravitational force on everything else, and developed his law of universal gravitation to explain the trajectories of cannonballs and the orbits of the planets (see page 34).

Another of nature's fundamental forces is **ELECTROMAGNETISM** (see page 38). In the 19th century, James Clerk Maxwell showed that electricity and magnetism were two sides of the same coin – moving charges can generate **MAGNETIC FIELDS**, while magnetic fields act on charged particles. These interactions are at the heart of every electric motor, mobile phone, and much more.

Light itself is an electromagnetic wave, composed of varying electric and magnetic fields endlessly chasing one another in a sinuous dance. Discovering that light is a form of electromagnetic radiation prompted a slew of discoveries, which eventually led to **ALBERT EINSTEIN**'s two theories of relativity (see page 40).

The **SPECIAL THEORY OF RELATIVITY** rests on the idea that the speed of light in a vacuum always seems to be the same, no matter whether the observer is standing still or moving. One bizarre consequence is that as you travel faster, time actually slows down. Another is that mass and energy are equivalent, as described by the iconic equation $E=mc^2$, so that one might think of matter as a condensed form of energy.

Einstein then developed the **GENERAL THEORY OF RELATIVITY**, concluding that masses 'warp' the fabric of the universe to cause what we perceive as **GRAVITY**. General relativity also predicted the existence of black holes (see page 42).

Many mysteries about energy and forces still remain unanswered. For example, astronomers think that galaxies must be held together with the help of unseen **DARK MATTER** and that the accelerating expansion of the universe is being driven by some kind of **DARK ENERGY** (see page 44). Solving these mysteries are among the greatest scientific challenges of the 21st century.

# ENERGY AND FORCES MAP

## MASS

### MAGNETIC FIELD
How the magnetic force is distributed around and within something magnetic, or as the result of an electric current.

### MAXWELL'S EQUATIONS
Four equations gathered by James Clerk Maxwell to describe properties of magnetic fields and electric charges, currents and fields, and how they relate to each other.

### ELECTRICAL CHARGE
Property of some subatomic particles that causes matter to experience a force in an electromagnetic field.

### FORCE
The push or pull on an object, either across a distance or when things touch. A force may make something move, change speed or change shape.

### ELECTROMAGNETISM
One of the fundamental forces in nature, centring on the interaction between electrically charged objects and the resulting magnetic fields.

### LAWS OF MOTION
Three laws published by Isaac Newton in 1687 that describe the relationships between forces acting on a body and its motion. These laws fail at atomic scales, or when objects travel close to the speed of light.

### GRAVITY
The attractive force between two objects, which depends on both their masses and their distance apart, according to Isaac Newton. For very large masses it is more accurately described by Albert Einstein's theory of general relativity.

### ISAAC NEWTON
English physicist and mathematician (1643–1727) who formulated the laws of motion and universal gravitation, among many achievements.

### DARK ENERGY
Hypothetical form of energy that acts like the opposite of gravity, proposed as the reason why the expansion of the universe is accelerating.

### DARK MATTER
Hypothetical form of invisible matter that makes up over 80 per cent of all matter in the universe and explains particular behaviour of stars, planets and galaxies.

# RELATIVITY

## THERMODYNAMICS
The science of the relationship between temperature, heat, work and energy.

## ENTROPY
A measure of the disorder and randomness of a system. In thermodynamics, increasing entropy means less thermal energy is available for doing useful work.

## ENERGY
The ability to 'do work'. Can be converted from one form (e.g. thermal, electrical or chemical) to another, but cannot be created or destroyed in a closed system, according to the law of conservation of energy.

## E=mc$^2$
Albert Einstein's equation showing the relationship between mass and energy, where **E** is energy, **m** is mass and **c** is the speed of light.

## SPECIAL THEORY OF RELATIVITY
Albert Einstein's 1905 theory that explains why the speed of light in a vacuum is the same for every observer, regardless of their motion or that of the source of light.

## GENERAL THEORY OF RELATIVITY
Albert Einstein's 1915 theory that explains gravity as being due to the warping of space-time by objects with mass.

## *ALBERT EINSTEIN*
Theoretical physicist (1879–1955) who developed the general and special theories of relativity and contributed to the development of quantum mechanics.

## BLACK HOLE
Astronomical objects so dense and with gravity so strong that nothing, not even light, can escape them.

## SPACE-TIME
The combination of three-dimensional space with a fourth dimension, which is time. An important concept in the general theory of relativity.

# Does everything obey Newton's laws of motion?

**⟶ Nearly everything! Newton's 300-year-old laws of motion have generally held true, but we now know of some scenarios where they don't survive scrutiny.**

Isaac Newton's three laws of motion are some of the most familiar and well-known concepts in the world of physics. We come across examples that demonstrate them every day. First published in 1687 in Newton's *Philosophiae Naturalis Principia Mathematica*, commonly known as the *Principia*, the first law states that a body that is at rest or moving at a constant speed will remain so. The second law is that the force acting upon an object is equal to the product of its mass and acceleration. And the third is that if two objects are exerting forces on one another, they will be equal in magnitude but opposite in direction.

These laws are more than 300 years old and in the majority of scenarios have been proven to be true. However, like many things in classical physics, they don't fare quite so well when we consider the extremes of the universe, at both the microscopic and macroscopic levels. For example, it turns out that subatomic particles do not work as you might expect from Newtonian physics,

and so at the smallest of scales, we instead need to turn to quantum mechanics (see page 68). Similarly, objects that travel at, or approaching, the speed of light, are also best described by different laws, including special and general relativity (see page 40).

We now know that instead of being an all-encompassing theory, Newton's laws of motion are, in fact, a special case that only holds true in what is referred to as an inertial frame of reference – that is, a frame of reference where, if no external force is applied to something, it will maintain the same velocity (which could be zero, meaning it is at rest).

In the case of non-inertial frames – for example, ones that are accelerating or rotating – scientists have introduced the concept of fictitious forces: the best known being the Coriolis force. When these extra forces are introduced, Newton's laws still work and thus continue to provide us with a solid foundation to build our understanding of physics, which is impressive for concepts that are now hundreds of years old.

# FICTITIOUS FORCES

A carousel, such as the one shown here, is actually a 'non-inertial frame of reference'. When you sit on the ride, you rotate along with it and experience one of the so-called 'fictitious forces' – that feeling of having to hold on so as not to be thrown off – which seems very real at the time! This is just one example where fictitious forces allow us to continue to apply Newton's laws to common situations.

# What goes up...?

→ ...must come down, so they say. Legend has it that Newton formulated his law of universal gravitation after seeing an apple fall from his tree. But some aspects of this law have also taken a fall.

Newton's famous law of universal gravitation states that two bodies in space pull on each other with an attractive force that is related to their masses and the distance between them. Before Newton's 1687 publication, scientists believed the force causing things to fall was a purely terrestrial phenomenon. However, when Newton saw his apple fall, the Moon was in the sky. He concluded the same force that was pulling the apple down – which he named gravity – also held the Moon in orbit. Newton's insight unified celestial and terrestrial gravity.

The theory says the gravitational force is directly proportional to the product of the two objects' masses and inversely proportional to the square of the distance between the two. Or put simply, the larger Earth holds the smaller Moon in orbit. It's universal and applies to any two (or more) masses anywhere, including stars and black holes (see page 42).

Combined with Newton's laws of motion – explaining how objects at a constant speed travel in straight lines unless acted on by another force – the law simply illustrates why moving planets remain in solar orbit.

Newton demonstrated this using a thought experiment. A cannonball dropped from a cliff falls vertically. Fired from a cannon it falls in an arc. However, if fired with sufficient velocity, it would go into orbit around Earth, just as planets orbit the Sun.

Physicist Henry Cavendish tested Newton's theory in 1798 using the attraction between two lead spheres to work out the specific gravity of Earth, from which its mass could be calculated. In 1846, Urbain Le Verrier predicted the existence of Neptune using Newtonian theory, by noting deviations in Uranus' orbit.

In 1915, Einstein's general theory of relativity (see page 40) offered an updated perspective on gravity, showing that large celestial masses significantly warp the space-time around them, pulling smaller masses into valleys created by the distortions. Subtle variations in the orbit of Mercury, unaccounted for by Newtonian gravity, can be explained by Einstein's theory; a consequence of a tiny planet close to the larger Sun being affected by space-time distortions around the star.

# UPDATING GRAVITY

Newton formulated his law of universal gravitation in the 17th century following on from earlier theories by Johannes Kepler, Galileo and Robert Hooke. Newton's law said the Moon orbits the Earth because of an attractive force between them. It held sway until 1915, when Einstein generalised his earlier special theory of relativity to include observers changing their speed, or accelerating. Einstein's realisation that acceleration is gravity meant his general theory of relativity was also a theory of gravity, which stated that mass – or energy – warps four-dimensional space-time, thus providing an alternative to Newton's law of gravitation.

# Why is thermodynamics a hot topic?

**→ Thermodynamics is the study of the heat, energy, work and temperature of a particular system. If the laws of thermodynamics varied just slightly, we would live in a very different world.**

It's a common misconception that thermodynamics is all about temperature – in reality it is much broader than that. Instead, it is about the study of thermal energy, which is the kinetic energy produced in atoms and molecules following an increase in temperature, and therefore the energy an object possesses due to internal motion.

The laws of thermodynamics may not be glamorous, but they are fundamental to our understanding of how things work and how to design and build things we rely on. Your car, the refrigerator in your kitchen and the rocket carrying the satellite that will tell your smartphone where you are all depend on our understanding of thermodynamics.

There are four fundamental laws of thermodynamics, which started to be developed in the early 19th century. The first law is a version of the law of conservation of energy, which says that for any isolated system, energy cannot be created or destroyed (although it can be transformed from one kind of energy to another). The second is that if an isolated system is not in equilibrium, 'entropy' always increases – entropy being a measure of the disorder and randomness of a system. And the third law says that as the temperature of a system approaches absolute zero, the entropy must approach a constant value.

Slightly confusingly, the fourth law is actually referred to as the zeroth law. This states that if two systems are in thermal equilibrium (they have the same temperature) with a third system, then they must also be in thermal equilibrium with one another.

These laws took many years to develop, but are important because thermodynamics underpins our knowledge of the universe on all scales.

Understanding thermodynamics changed our world – and continues to do so. It led to the development of steam trains and internal combustion engines, and is now applied to increasingly advanced rockets and space missions. It is also informing our development of renewable sources of energy (see page 130), as applying the laws of thermodynamics can help engineers to improve the efficiency with which, for example, solar or wind energy can be converted into useful forms.

# LAWS OF THERMODYNAMICS

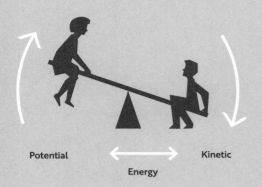

Potential

Energy

Kinetic

## FIRST LAW OF THERMODYNAMICS

*Energy cannot be created or destroyed but it can be transformed from one kind of energy to another.*

Heat transfer

Hot

Cold

## SECOND LAW OF THERMODYNAMICS

*If an isolated system is not in equilibrium, 'entropy' always increases. One consequence is that heat flows from hot things to cold things.*

Perfect crystal
at absolute zero

## THIRD LAW OF THERMODYNAMICS

*A perfect crystal at a temperature of absolute zero (-273°C) has zero entropy.*

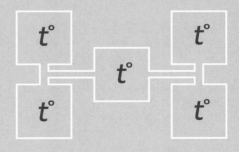

## ZEROTH LAW

*If any two systems are in thermal equilibrium with a third system, then they are also in thermal equilibrium with each other.*

# How much does electromagnetism charge?

→ **Electromagnetism is one of the key pillars of everyday physics. It centres on how electrically charged objects interact with one another, and how this interaction results in magnetic fields.**

The theory of electromagnetism relates to many concepts in physics, including electric currents, electric fields and magnetic fields, and the theorems that link them all.

A fundamental property of all objects is electrical charge – every object has an electric field intrinsically associated with it. Electrical charge can either be negative, positive or neutral. When two oppositely charged objects are placed next to each other, they are attracted to one another – opposites attract! Conversely, when two identically charged objects are placed next to each other, they repel one another.

In each case, as the charged particles begin to move, another field is also created – a magnetic field. This magnetic field causes an additional force on charged particles, and this effect has numerous uses in everyday life.

These properties were studied independently by many physicists and mathematicians, but none managed to mathematically describe electromagnetism in its entirety until the mid-1800s. It was then that a physicist called James Clerk Maxwell took known equations and unified them into a coherent package, now known as Maxwell's equations.

Four distinct equations combine to form Maxwell's equations, including formulae from famous physicists Carl Friedrich Gauss, André-Marie Ampère and Michael Faraday. Gauss contributed the first two formulae of Maxwell's equations, describing the behaviour of electric fields and then descriptions of the magnetic fields. The third Maxwell equation is known as Faraday's Law, which describes how electrical currents can be induced in a wire when a changing magnetic field is present. The final law is Ampère's Law, with a key term added by Maxwell, which states how magnetic fields can also be generated by changing electric fields.

The implications of Maxwell's equations cannot be overstated. Countless pieces of technology used in everyday life are under-pinned by Maxwell's equations, including electric motors, power generation and wireless communication.

# ELECTROMAGNETISM BY MAXWELL

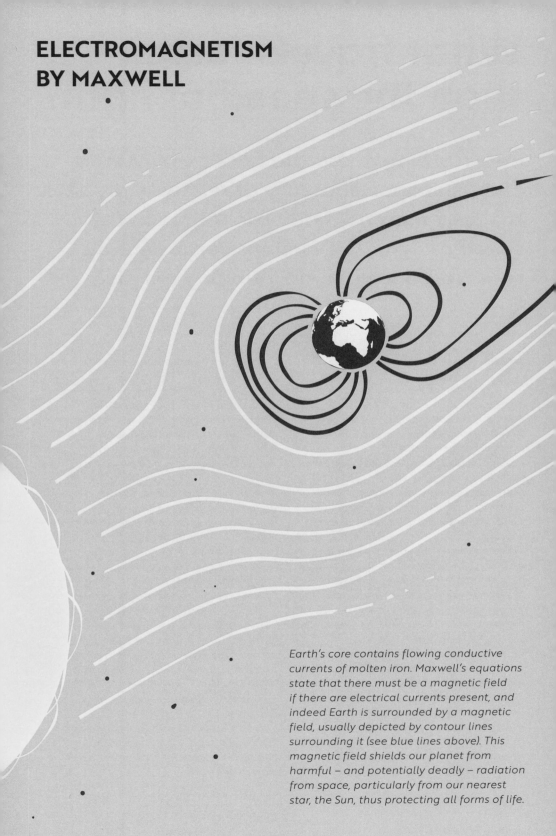

Earth's core contains flowing conductive currents of molten iron. Maxwell's equations state that there must be a magnetic field if there are electrical currents present, and indeed Earth is surrounded by a magnetic field, usually depicted by contour lines surrounding it (see blue lines above). This magnetic field shields our planet from harmful – and potentially deadly – radiation from space, particularly from our nearest star, the Sun, thus protecting all forms of life.

# What travels faster than the speed of light?

⟶ **Nothing does. And here's why. Albert Einstein's special theory of relativity dictates that any material body cannot reach the speed of light in a vacuum because to do so it would have to be infinitely massive.**

Albert Einstein theorised that individual observers see events differently depending on their relative speed. Hence relativity. He arrived at this conclusion after realising the laws of optics are the same for every observer, no matter what their speed.

Specifically, Einstein's special theory of relativity, published in 1905, postulated that every observer measures the same speed of light in a vacuum: 299,792,458 metres per second. It is invariant. But conundrums exist. Why is it the same for all observers regardless of their relative motion or the motion of the light source? Why doesn't the beam from a torch strapped to a speeding rocket travel faster than light? Something strange must happen to space and time. Einstein concluded the motion of an object slows time, and space shrinks in the direction of its motion.

He was proved correct. Clocks on airliners tick marginally slower than identical ones on the ground. It's called time dilation.

Another strange consequence of special relativity is that mass and energy can be interconverted, according to $E=mc^2$.

In 1915, Einstein generalised his theory to include observers changing speed, or accelerating. He also realised acceleration *is* gravity – his general theory of relativity was also a theory of gravity.

General relativity combines the three spatial dimensions with a fourth, which is time, to create what is referred to as space-time. The theory says huge masses, such as stars, warp this four-dimensional space-time. That's all gravity is: warped space-time. Whereas Newton's law of gravitation said Earth orbits the Sun because of an attractive force between them, general relativity says gravity is the consequence of the Sun's mass creating a valley in the space-time around it.

Hold a bedsheet taut and drop a medicine ball onto it. It deforms, creating a dip around the ball. A marble, rolled onto the sheet runs towards the depression, mimicking Earth's orbit around the Sun. What we perceive as gravity is the altered geometry of space-time. Similarly, Earth-bound observers will perceive gravitational lensing, which is starlight bending as it passes the Sun, as predicted by Einstein.

He also foresaw gravitational waves caused by cataclysmic events such as colliding black holes. These ripples of undulating space-time travel at light speed, providing information about the universe's origins.

# TIME DILATION

When cosmonaut Sergei Krikalev returned to Earth in 1992 after a mammoth and unexpected 311-day stay in space, he was 0.02 of a second younger than he would have been had he stayed on Earth. This was because of the speed he had been travelling around the planet compared with his earthbound colleagues (and the rest of us). He had benefited ever so slightly from the time dilation predicated by Einstein.

# How can we spot a black hole?

⟶ Long after they were first predicted, we now have verifiable evidence of the existence of black holes. But to spot one, you need to know what you are looking for. And, more importantly, you need to know where to look.

Albert Einstein foresaw the existence of black holes in his 1915 general theory of relativity – objects so dense and with gravity so strong that nothing, not even light, could escape them.

Later, Subrahmanyan Chandrasekhar, who won the 1938 Nobel Prize in Physics, applied the burgeoning theories of quantum mechanics to his studies of dying stars. He realised that if a star is above a certain mass, the gravitational force it exerts is so large that when it dies it collapses to an infinitely small dot. He had predicted what would later be termed black holes.

To understand the extreme forces involved, consider the bedsheet analogy for space-time (see page 40). Imagine the medicine ball staying the same size but its mass increasing. As it does, the sheet will deform further until its sides touch above the ball. This gives you an idea of what occurs in the real universe. The distorted fabric of space-time wraps itself around the dense mass, disconnecting it from everything. Nothing can escape its gravity. It has become a black hole.

At the centre of a black hole is a point of infinite density, known as a singularity. Its boundary is called the event horizon – nothing inside can cross this and break free, including light.

Astronomers believe four types of black hole may exist. Stellar-mass black holes are caused by collapsing stars as predicted by Chandrasekhar. Supermassive black holes, predicted by Einstein, form at the centre of galaxies, including our Milky Way. The smallest class, proposed by cosmologist Stephen Hawking, remains theoretical. These mini-black holes could have formed shortly after the Big Bang (see page 14) and then evaporated, leaving behind the enigmatic phenomenon of gamma-ray bursts. And there may be a fourth class of intermediate black holes.

So can we spot them? Not exactly, but we can listen for radio sources or radiation associated with them and detect their presence through the influence they exert on matter nearby, dragging gases towards them or affecting the movements of nearby stars, betraying their position.

# DETECTING AN EVENT HORIZON

Can you see a black hole? Despite their mass they are relatively small in size, so our best telescopes working alone cannot see them. The Event Horizon Telescope, on the other hand, is a virtual observatory made up of telescopes spanning the planet from Greenland to Antarctica, searching for phenomena associated with black holes. In 2019, it captured the first image ever of a black hole – or, more specifically, the ring of light produced by matter as it is gobbled up by the supermassive black hole at the centre of our neighbouring galaxy M87. The mass of this black hole is 6.5 billion times that of our Sun.

# Why does dark matter matter?

→ **Because without it, the universe as we know it simply doesn't add up. We can't see it, yet we know it's there because of the effect it has on other objects we can observe, such as stars and galaxies.**

No quest in modern cosmology has greater significance than the search for dark matter and dark energy. During the last century, cosmologists realised visible galaxies of stars represent only a fraction of the mass of the universe. The rest we cannot see – it neither emits nor absorbs light. It is known as dark matter.

We know it's there because something greater than gravity alone acts on the motion of galaxies. As they spin they should tear apart, yet they don't. In 1997, the Hubble Space Telescope revealed light bending around a star cluster, something requiring 250 times more force than the gravity produced by those stars. Dark matter is holding everything together like dough filling the gaps between currants in a bun.

So what is it? Theories abound. Part of its mass may be the kind of ordinary stuff we find in our own solar system, say Jupiter-sized objects too distant to observe. Or perhaps it comprises bodies known as machos (massive compact halo objects),

which include black holes. Others think it may comprise particles created when the universe was young, including WIMPS (weakly interacting massive particles). The search for these is a cosmological holy grail.

But there's a complicating factor. While dark matter acts like an attracting force, slowing the universe's expansion, dark energy seems to do the opposite. Distant galaxies are moving away faster than those nearby, indicating something is causing expansion to accelerate. This dark energy may account for nearly 70 per cent of the universe's mass, far more than dark matter. Again, its composition is unknown. It may comprise temporary particles that form and then disappear. Or is it a type of dynamic energy dubbed 'quintessence'? Maybe it's simply a property of space itself.

Whatever they are, dark matter and dark energy hold the key to comprehending how galaxies evolve and to helping explain the future of our universe. Will it continue expanding, stabilise or ultimately collapse?

# BALANCING THE CELESTIAL SCALES

When we think of a galaxy, we think of spirals of stars swimming against the blackness of space. But this familiar image represents only a tiny fraction of what is out there. Something else was required to balance the cosmological scales. If the visible universe fills the left-hand scale above, what is on the right? Originally astronomers called it 'missing mass', but that was a misnomer. Nothing was missing, it was just invisible. In 1933, Fritz Zwicky pointed out that there was more gravitational force holding together the Coma Cluster of galaxies than could be accounted for by what we could see. That set the ball rolling in the search for dark matter, which is still ongoing nearly a century later.

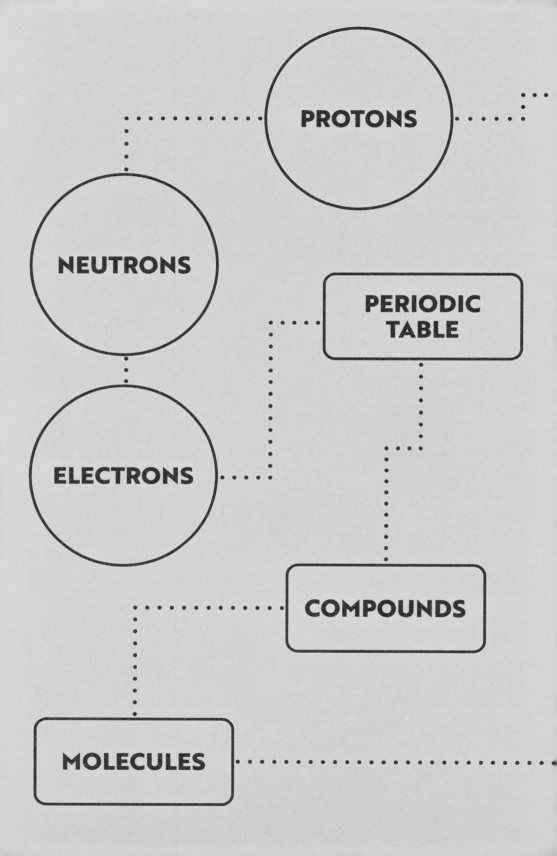

ELEMENTS

# CHAPTER 3

MATTER

REACTIONS

NANOTECHNOLOGY

CHIRAL

# INTRODUCTION

**A**TOMS are the building blocks of everyday matter. The scientific journey to understand what they are, and how we can manipulate them, has taken more than 2,000 years. The concept dates back to the 5th century BCE, when the Greek philosopher Democritus suggested that everything was built from tiny, invisible and indivisible nuggets (see page 52).

By the 19th century, scientists were getting to grips with atoms, as they discovered more chemical **ELEMENTS**. These are pure substances – such as hydrogen or gold – that **CHEMICAL REACTIONS** cannot break down into simpler materials. Each element is composed solely of its own unique kind of atom. Once scientists learned how to cut deeper, they found that each atom contains a nucleus (inner core) of **PROTONS** and (usually) **NEUTRONS**, surrounded by **ELECTRONS**. The number of protons determines the element: hydrogen atoms always have one proton, while gold atoms always have 79.

Chemists needed to organise their growing list of elements, and in 1869 **DMITRI MENDELEEV** devised a way to group elements by the weights of their atoms, along with their chemical and physical properties. This is the **PERIODIC TABLE**, which has evolved into a detailed atlas that helps scientists to navigate the elements (see page 54). It corrals families of elements that have similar chemical reactivity, and reveals how that reactivity changes from light to heavy atoms.

Chemical elements often team up to form **COMPOUNDS**. This involves chemical reactions that stick atoms together, or separate them from one another. The stickiness that binds atoms together is called a **CHEMICAL BOND**. By tweaking chemical bonds and rearranging atoms, scientist's can take simple **MOLECULES** extracted from oil and turn them into powerful anticancer medicines, or flexible phone displays, or millions of other substances (see page 56).

Yet even if two molecules have identical atoms connected by identical bonds, they can sometimes have very different properties, because of the particular spatial arrangement of their atoms. A molecule called carvone, for example, has two forms that are mirror images of each other, and cannot be superimposed – just like your left and right hands. It is therefore said to be chiral (see page 58). The consequence for carvone is that its right-handed form has a spearmint scent, while left-handed carvone smells like caraway seeds. **CHIRALITY** steers many other aspects of biology, from the DNA that carries genetic information in your cells, to the amino acids that make up every protein in your body.

In the 1980s, scientists developed techniques to produce astonishing images of individual atoms or molecules. These mapped the miniaturised realm of **NANOTECHNOLOGY**, which has produced faster computer chips and the minuscule glowing dots that light up the latest TV screens (see page 60). It has also revealed hidden mysteries: for at the nanoscale, the normal properties of bulk matter become tinged with the bizarre effects of the quantum realm.

# MATTER MAP

## CHEMISTRY

### PERIODIC TABLE
An iconic graphic formulation of the chemical elements, in which blocks, rows (periods) and columns (groups) depict trends in the elements based upon their electron configurations.

### ATOMIC NUMBER (Z)
The number identifying a chemical element, equal to the number of protons in its nuclei.

### ELEMENT
A substance consisting only of atoms with the same number of protons in their nuclei, which cannot be broken down into simpler substances by chemical reaction.

### PROTON (P)
A positively charged subatomic particle found in the nucleus of an atom, where the number of protons present gives an element its atomic number.

### ATOM
The smallest unit of ordinary matter, composed of a positively charged nucleus surrounded by a cloud of negatively charged electrons, bound together by electrostatic force.

### NUCLEUS
The dense region at the centre of an atom, where neutrons and positively charged protons are bound together by the nuclear force.

### ELECTRON
A negatively charged subatomic particle with a mass of about 1/1,836th of a proton.

### NEUTRON (N)
A subatomic particle with neutral charge, found in the nucleus of an atom.

### ISOTOPE
Two or more types of atom with the same number of protons but different numbers of neutrons are isotopes of the same element.

### ION
Atom with a positive or negative charge due to a mismatch between the number of electrons and protons.

## CATALYSTS

**DMITRI MENDELEEV**
The Russian chemist (1834–1907) who formulated the periodic law and devised the first periodic table to predict the properties of as-yet-undiscovered elements.

**DEMOCRITUS**
Ancient Greek philosopher (around 460–370 BCE) who proposed that everything was made up from tiny pieces of matter called atoms, instead of combinations of earth, air, fire and water.

**COMPOUND**
A chemical substance composed of many identical molecules made up of atoms from different elements bound together by a chemical bond.

**NANOTECHNOLOGY**
Technology at an extremely small scale – a nanometre is one billionth of a metre.

**MOLECULE**
A group of two or more atoms, without electrical charge, held together by chemical bonds.

**CHEMICAL BOND**
The attraction between atoms (negative electrons and positive protons attract each other) that enables compounds to form and dictates the structure of matter.

**CHEMICAL REACTION**
The chemical transformation of one substance into another, most commonly through the position of electrons in forming and breaking chemical bonds.

**CHIRALITY**
When something is the 'mirror image' of another, such as our hands, and cannot be superimposed on the other by any means. In molecules, this may give them different properties.

# How did the atom split scientists?

**→ Philosophers and scientists spent thousands of years arguing about what the stuff around us is made of. The discovery that atoms are the building blocks of matter settled the debate and laid down one of the most important foundations of science.**

Philosophers such as Aristotle and Plato were convinced that everything was composed of four elements – earth, air, fire and water – mixed together in different proportions. For centuries most scientists agreed with them, but there were a few outspoken rebels. Back in the 5th century BCE for example, the Greek philosopher Democritus proposed that the world and everything in it was built from tiny, uncuttable nuggets of matter called atoms.

Fast forward two millennia and Democritus had the last laugh. By the turn of the 19th century, scientists had already figured out that gases were probably made of minuscule particles. Then John Dalton, the Cumberland-born son of a weaver, reasoned that this must be true of all matter.

Dalton suggested that there are many different types of atom, each with unique properties. When lots of atoms of a single type are gathered together, they form a pure element – for example, gold or sulfur – which cannot be broken down into simpler materials by chemical reactions. When different types of atoms are combined, they form compounds, such as water or table salt.

Dalton was absolutely right. We now know that there are 94 different types of atoms that occur naturally, each of which is the basic building block of a unique element (see page 54). Atoms are so small that trillions of them fit into the full stop at the end of this sentence. They can stick together, much like LEGO® bricks, in an incredible variety of combinations, forming structures called molecules.

It took another 100 years or so for scientists to figure out that atoms are themselves made up of smaller particles. At the heart of every atom is a nucleus, containing positively-charged protons and neutral neutrons, surrounded by enough negatively-charged electrons to balance the protons' charge. The only exception is hydrogen, the lightest element, whose atoms contain only a proton and an electron. The number of protons – the atomic number – determines the identity of the element; for example, if there are 79 protons, the atom is always gold.

# INSIDE THE ATOM

All carbon nuclei have six protons and most have six neutrons. But a few have seven neutrons, or even eight. These variants of elements, called isotopes (see page 18), are named according to their sum total of protons and neutrons. Some, like carbon-14, are radioactive – their unstable nuclei spontaneously split apart to release radiation. When scientists learned how to trigger this breakdown in a uranium isotope, it ushered in the era of nuclear power stations and atom bombs. Once, the atom had split scientists; now, scientists were splitting the atom.

## CARBON-12

- Six protons
- Six neutrons
- Six electrons

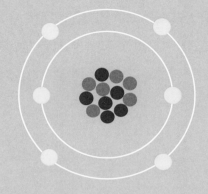

## CARBON-13

- Six protons
- Seven neutrons
- Six electrons

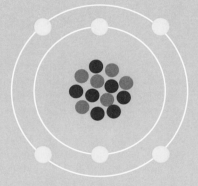

## CARBON-14

- Six protons
- Eight neutrons
- Six electrons

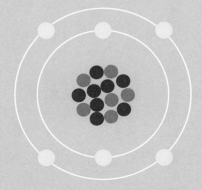

# Can the periodic table predict the future?

→ Yes! The periodic table organises chemical elements into rows and columns; early versions featured gaps for as-yet-undiscovered elements, giving scientists a road map to find the missing materials.

Soon after scientists realised that each chemical element was made up of its own unique atoms (see page 52), they started to organise the elements according to the weights of those atoms. Hydrogen, the lightest element, was assigned an atomic weight of one, and carbon atoms, for example, an atomic weight of twelve.

By 1869, the list of elements had grown to more than 60. Then, in March of that year, Russian chemist Dmitri Mendeleev proposed a novel way to organise the building blocks of the universe, based on the connections atoms make with one another.

When different atoms team up to make compounds, they behave as if they have a number of 'hooks' to snag partners in an atomic dance (see page 56). Hydrogen, for example, has only one hook, while oxygen has two, which is why water contains two atoms of hydrogen for every atom of oxygen and its chemical formula is $H_2O$. The number of connections an atom can make is its valence.

Mendeleev noticed that when he listed some elements by their atomic weight, the valences of these atoms rose and fell in a periodic pattern. So he arranged the list in rows, one beneath the other, with all the atoms in one column having the same valence and similar chemical properties. When there was no suitable element to fill a particular spot, he left a gap and declared it would be occupied by an as-yet undiscovered element.

This gave chemists an atlas of elements that had enormous predictive power. It gave clues about how elements were likely to react together and guided them to discover new elements, because the position of the gaps revealed which compounds might host the missing materials. Gallium, for example, was discovered just a few years later. Its properties were a perfect match for those expected of the element missing from its allotted space in the table.

Since then, the periodic table has been redrawn many times, as scientists found better ways to fit elements together (now ordering them by atomic number, not atomic weight), but they are still based on Mendeleev's original concept.

# A GROWING MAP

Over the years, Mendeleev's relatively simple periodic table has evolved into a detailed map of the elements. Some scientists have reshaped it into spirals, flowers and ribbons (although not yet a beard). The standard table now includes super-heavy artificial elements created in huge atom-smashing machines. Element 106, seaborgium, is named in honour of Glenn Seaborg, an American chemist who helped to discover ten of the heaviest elements.

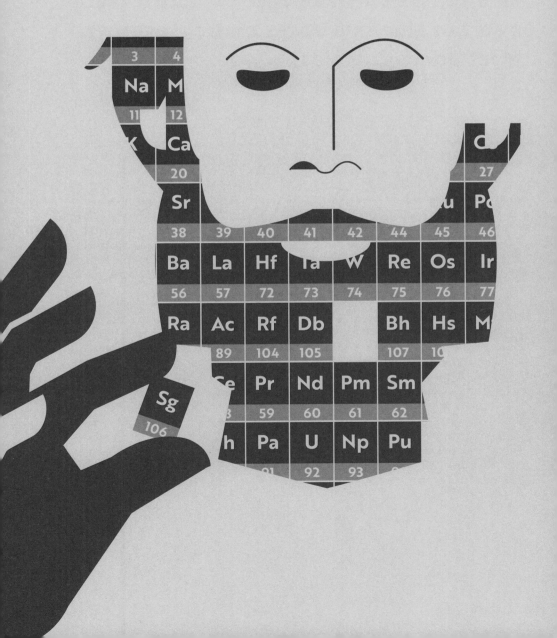

# Are there secret agents in a chemical bond?

**→ There certainly are. In the spaces around atoms, tiny charged particles called electrons are shaken and stirred to create a sort of glue that sticks matter together. Meet Bond, Chemical Bond.**

Electrons are amazing things. These almost infinitesimally small points of negative charge zip through the electrical cables in our homes to power our appliances. But electrons are more than mere electricity carriers – without them, the world as we know it would simply fall apart.

Atoms contain a positive nucleus surrounded by negative electrons (see page 52). One way to think of electrons is as if they orbit the nucleus like planets around the Sun, with some closer in and others farther away. These layers can accommodate different numbers of electrons – the first holds two electrons, the second fits eight, the third eighteen, and so on. It is this underlying structure that determines the uneven shape of the periodic table (see page 54).

An atom's outermost electrons are largely responsible for its chemistry; they determine the number of 'hooks' an atom has to link up with other atoms. Much of chemistry is about how these clouds of electrons move around and weave fresh bonds between atoms.

Sometimes, an atom can give one or more of its electrons to another atom; this leaves the donor positively charged and the recipient negatively charged. These charged atoms are called ions, and the attraction between their opposite charges is an ionic bond. These bonds help ions to stack up in repeating three-dimensional patterns, like fruit on a greengrocer's stall, to form crystals such as sodium chloride – better known as plain old table salt.

In 1916, the American chemist Gilbert Lewis realised that some atoms aren't quite as generous and prefer to share their electrons rather than give them away. When a pair of shared electrons occupies the space between two atoms they can form a covalent bond. These bonds unite the atoms of many carbon-based molecules, from the petrol in your car to the DNA in your cells, and they also ensure that diamonds are forever (well, almost).

Electrons can make all kinds of other types of bonds, too, proving to be chemistry's very own secret agent.

# IONIC BONDING IN SODIUM CHLORIDE

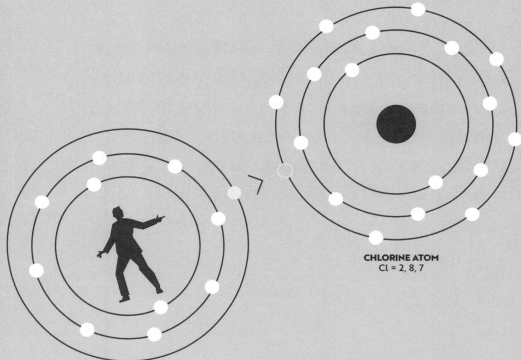

**CHLORINE ATOM**
Cl = 2, 8, 7

**SODIUM ATOM**
Na = 2, 8, 1

*Ionic compounds are formed when atoms swap electrons to form charged ions that stick together in large crystalline lattices. To make table salt, for example, an atom of sodium gives away an electron to chlorine, neatly filling a gap in its outermost ring of electrons. (The total electrons in each ring, or 'shell', are typically written as a series of numbers.) Drawing electrons as if they were bullets fired from James Bond's Walther PPK pistol certainly makes it easier to see how they move. But quantum mechanics (page 68) has revealed that the electrons around atoms are actually more like clouds, with the thicker parts of the cloud showing where an electron is likely to be found.*

# Is chirality just a sleight of hand?

→ It might look like a conjuring trick, but chirality reveals how some molecules that appear to be identical are actually mirror images of one another. Many molecules in your body are chiral, so medicines often need to be chiral too.

Take a look at your hands. They seem pretty similar, with four fingers and a thumb connected to a palm. But they are clearly different – your hands are mirror images of each other.

A lot of molecules have exactly the same kind of handedness, which is a property known as chirality. A pair of chiral molecules have the same atoms, connected by the same bonds, but the spatial arrangement of their atoms makes them mirror images of each other.

This is no esoteric quirk of the molecular world. The molecules of DNA that store genetic information in your cells are all twisted into a right-handed helix, while the proteins that form your skin, muscles and hair are built almost exclusively from left-handed amino acids. Nobody knows why life ended up choosing these particular chiral forms, but it has profound implications.

Many medicines work by binding to proteins, so they are often dispensed in just one of their two chiral forms. One may be less effective than the other, or even have adverse side-effects, due to the different ways that two chiral molecules can stick together. For example, left-handed ibuprofen is an effective painkiller, whereas right-handed ibuprofen is not.

French physicist Jean-Baptiste Biot caught the first glimpse of chirality in 1815 when he noticed that some substances could rotate a beam of polarised light either clockwise or anticlockwise. In 1848, French chemist Louis Pasteur managed to separate left- and right-handed crystals of tartaric acid, and proved they rotated light in opposite directions because of the way their molecules were arranged.

Pasteur speculated it might be possible to create a mirror-image form of life, using the 'wrong' mirror forms of biological molecules. Scientists are now turning Pasteur's idea into reality, by painstakingly building looking-glass versions of DNA, proteins and the biochemical machinery that handles these molecules. Mirror-proteins are also being tested as medicines; these can be programmed to attack specific targets, such as cancer cells, but their alien chirality means they cannot be broken down by our body's usual defence systems.

# HANDY MOLECULES

The chemical carvone is chiral – it can
exist in two mirror-image forms. Left-handed
carvone smells like caraway seeds, whereas
right-handed carvone smells of spearmint.
Scientists are still trying to figure out why
this is the case, because the two chiral
forms of other molecules don't always
smell different, so our sense of smell
isn't inherently chiral.

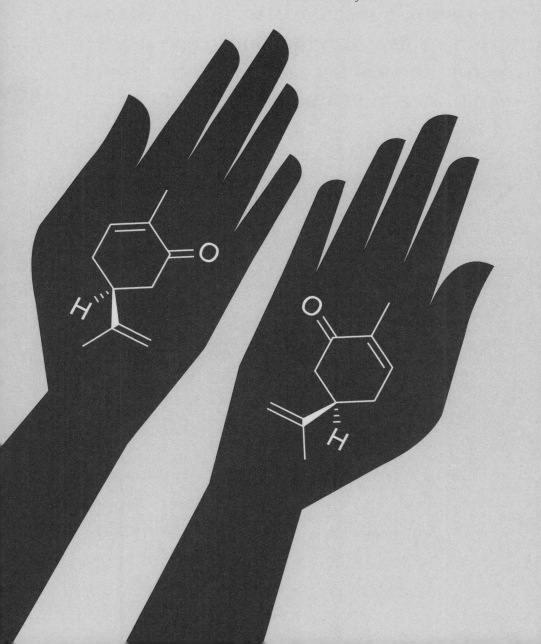

# How do we navigate at the nanoscale?

**⟶ With a very small map, of course. The nanoscale is measured in mere billionths of a metre, but scientists can pick their way through this Lilliputian landscape using instruments that are able to detect and manipulate individual atoms.**

Nanotechnology is the science of the exceedingly small. Explorers in this microcosm measure their journeys by the nanometre, or a billionth of a metre – the length of three atoms of gold arranged in a line. If you were just one nanometre tall, a single SARS-CoV-2 coronavirus would seem as big as St Paul's Cathedral. And while the science may be small, it is having a huge impact on our lives.

The nanoworld started to swim into view in the 1980s, when several powerful new microscopes were developed by scientists at IBM. The scanning tunnelling microscope relies on a very sharp tip held just above a surface, close enough for electrons to hop across the gap. As the tip moves around, changes in the current of electrons can be turned into images of atoms and molecules on the surface. Meanwhile, the atomic force microscope produces similar images by using its sharp tip to directly sense the texture of the surface, rather like the needle of a record player bobbing up and down in the grooves of an LP.

These instruments have helped scientists develop and study a vast array of nanomaterials. Take catalysts, the substances that speed up chemical reactions. Chemists can boost the activity of catalysts by breaking them down into nanoparticles, each containing just a few dozen atoms. These kinds of nanoparticle catalysts help to produce molecules that are used to make plastics and medicines.

Quantum dots are a type of nanoparticle made from semiconductor materials and they are now being used to light up our TV screens. By fine-tuning the sizes and composition of these dots, they can be made to emit different colours when illuminated by a blue backlight.

Nanotechnology also helps to shrink electronic components and squeeze ever more computing power onto silicon chips. In 1970, the core of a computer chip's transistors was about 1,000 nanometres wide. Thanks to techniques such as nanolithography, which uses ultraviolet light as a scalpel to carve materials into exquisitely small shapes, those parts are now just five nanometres wide.

# CONSTRUCTION IN THE NANO WORLD

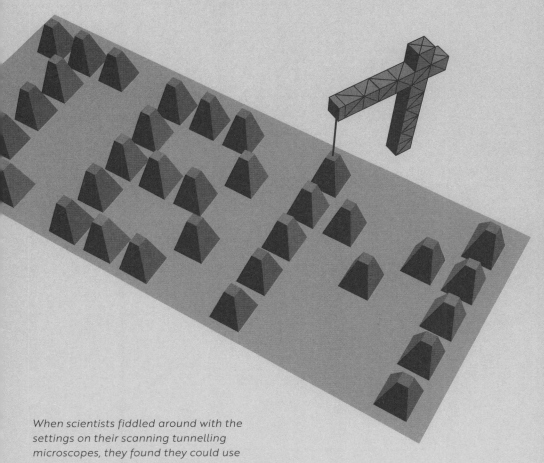

When scientists fiddled around with the settings on their scanning tunnelling microscopes, they found they could use them as nanoscale cranes to move atoms around – spelling out the initials 'IBM' using xenon atoms, for example. Nobel Prize-winning physicist and keen bongo player Richard Feynman famously predicted this kind of technology in his 1959 lecture entitled 'There's Plenty of Room at the Bottom'. It's debatable how much the lecture influenced early developments in nanotechnology, but many of its proposals did come true.

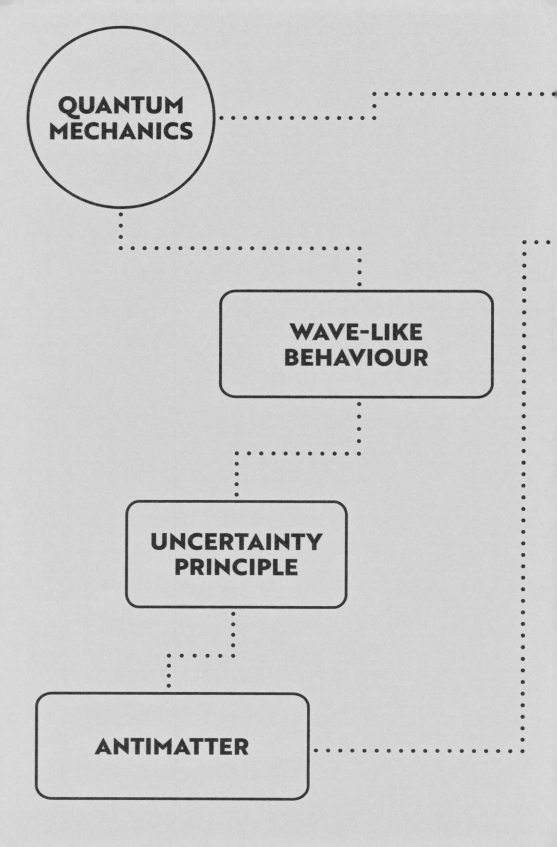

# CHAPTER 4

FOUNDATIONS

STANDARD MODEL

SUBATOMIC PARTICLES

NEUTRINOS

# INTRODUCTION

In the previous two chapters, we explored the energy and forces that drive change in the universe and the matter that makes up the everyday world. But some of the most important advances in 20th-century physics came from diving beneath the skin of reality and into the strange realm of quantum mechanics and subatomic particles.

**QUANTUM MECHANICS** describes how matter and energy interact at subatomic scales. One of the big ideas behind quantum mechanics is that energy isn't measured like a piece of string, which can have any length you like – instead it comes in discrete chunks, which physicist Max Planck called 'quanta' (see page 68). This sparked a whole slew of discoveries that helped to build modern quantum physics.

For example, 19th-century scientists had shown that light was made of waves that could diffract and interfere like ripples in a pond. But Albert Einstein and others found that light can also behave as if it were a stream of particles called **PHOTONS**, and that things traditionally thought of as particles, such as electrons, can act like waves. This chameleon-like behaviour is known as **WAVE-PARTICLE DUALITY** (see page 70).

The wave nature of particles leads to an underlying ambiguity about the subatomic world. The **UNCERTAINTY PRINCIPLE** says that it is impossible to know both the precise location and momentum of a particle at the same time – as you pin down one of these properties with more precision, the other inevitably becomes more fuzzy (see page 72).

Meanwhile, quantum mechanics also correctly predicted the existence of **ANTIMATTER** particles such as the **POSITRON**, which has exactly the same mass as an electron but carries an opposite charge (see page 74).

All of the fundamental particles discovered by physicists are housed within a grand theoretical framework known as the **STANDARD MODEL** (see page 76). In this menagerie, some particles make up the matter around us, while others are responsible for carrying fundamental forces such as electromagnetism. One of the force carriers is called the **HIGGS BOSON**, long predicted by the Standard Model and finally discovered in 2012 (see page 80). The Higgs boson is a manifestation of a field that gives other particles their mass – it also explains why photons of light have no mass at all.

But there are still some big gaps in the Standard Model. One problem comes in the form of **NEUTRINOS**, which are produced during certain kinds of radioactive decay and do not behave as the Model predicts (see page 78). Another problem is that the Model does not include gravity, so physicists are hunting for new theories of 'quantum gravity' to fix that. After more than a century spent exploring the quantum world, it seems that the foundations of reality run deeper still.

# FOUNDATIONS MAP

**PARTICLES**

**PHOTON**
An elementary particle, in the class of bosons, which is massless so always moves at the speed of light in a vacuum.

**PARTICLE DETECTOR**
Experiments to detect particles, their attributes and their interactions. Typically very large and built underground to shield them from sources of radiation.

**BOSON**
One of two fundamental classes of subatomic particles along with fermions. Bosons include gluons, the Higgs boson and mesons.

**HIGGS BOSON**
An elementary particle in the Standard Model produced by the quantum excitation of the Higgs field, which generates mass for massless bosons through their interaction with it.

**STANDARD MODEL**
A framework for understanding fundamental physics, classifying the known elementary particles and three of the four fundamental forces (strong nuclear force, weak nuclear force, electromagnetism).

**FUNDAMENTAL PARTICLE**
In particle physics, the fundamental or elementary particles are excitations of the quantum fields, and include photons, neutrinos and bosons.

**FERMION**
One of two fundamental classes of subatomic particles along with bosons. Fermions include quarks, leptons and baryons.

**POSITRON**
Particle identical to an electron but with a positive charge – the antiparticle of an electron.

**NEUTRINO**
Fundamental particle with tiny mass and no electrical charge. Known to exist in three slightly different types, or 'flavours': electron neutrino, muon neutrino and tau neutrino.

**POSITRON EMISSION TOMOGRAPHY**
Medical imaging procedure: radioactive isotopes are injected into a patient to produce positrons that emit gamma rays when they annihilate with electrons.

# QUANTUM

## DOUBLE SLIT EXPERIMENT

Experiment used to demonstrate wave-particle duality by shining light through two parallel slits onto a flat surface and viewing the resulting patterns.

## WAVE-PARTICLE DUALITY

When particles appear to behave like both particles and waves – a key concept in quantum mechanics.

## QUANTUM MECHANICS

Branch of physics that describes atoms and subatomic particles, and how they move and interact.

## UNCERTAINTY PRINCIPLE

Published in 1927 by Werner Heisenberg, this states that it is impossible to precisely measure both the position and momentum of a particle simultaneously.

## ENTANGLEMENT

When two particles remain linked together, no matter how far apart they are, and share a common, unified state.

## SCHRÖDINGER'S CAT

Thought experiment illustrating a paradox of quantum superposition, based on the impossibility of knowing if a cat in a box is alive or dead if its fate depends on a random subatomic event.

## ANTIMATTER

The oppositely charged twin of ordinary matter. Antiparticles have the same mass but opposite charge: for example, a positron is a positively charged electron.

## PAUL DIRAC

English physicist (1902–84) who brought together quantum mechanics and special relativity in the Dirac Equation, and predicted the existence of antiparticles.

# Who put the quantum in quantum mechanics?

⟶ **Isaac Newton's equations well describe the motion of objects we see and interact with in everyday life. But tiny subatomic particles behave in an entirely different manner, governed by the laws of quantum mechanics.**

⤵ Quantum mechanics describes how subatomic particles move and interact, including many unintuitive and quirky behaviours. The origins of quantum mechanics dates back to the early 1900s, when the German physicist Max Planck was studying the basic physics behind hot glowing matter. Planck determined that energy is quantised, meaning that it comes in separate packets and not as a continuous stream. Although simple on the surface, the implications of this were profound. Planck's ground-breaking work would earn him the Nobel Prize in 1918, laying the foundation for the birth of quantum mechanics.

If energy was indeed quantised as Planck showed, then the interaction between energy and particles must also be quantised. This was first shown by arguably the world's most famous physicist, Albert Einstein. If light is shone onto a metal, energy from the light is transferred to the electrons within the metal. If each packet of light carries enough energy, then the electrons will be knocked from their atoms and ejected from the metal. If each packet of light does not carry enough energy, then no electrons are emitted, no matter what quantity of light packets fall onto the metal. This is now known as the photoelectric effect, and won Einstein the Nobel Prize in 1905.

The work of Einstein and Planck would lead the way for countless more branches of quantum mechanics. These fields include the concepts of wave-particle duality (see page 70), quantum entanglement and the oft-quoted Heisenberg's uncertainty principle (see page 72). Famous physicists such as Richard Feynman and Paul Dirac would also add to the ever-expanding field of quantum mechanics, with contributions in the form of quantum electrodynamics and quantum field theory, both of which describe the interactions between quantised particles.

The field of quantum mechanics is still growing, and now permeates into the technology we come to rely on in everyday life, which will one day include quantum computing (see page 154) – something that would surely have delighted both Planck and Einstein.

# THE PHOTOELECTRIC EFFECT

A simple analogy to understand the photoelectric effect is that of a coconut shy. In this analogy, particles of light (photons, represented above by yellow balls) strike a metal sheet (represented by the coconut). Here, larger balls represent photons of higher energies. In a coconut shy, only the heavy balls will knock over the coconut because they have most energy. Similarly, only the most energetic photons will eject an electron from a metal.

# When is a particle also a wave?

**→ Electrons are some of the smallest particles we know. But even though we think of them as particles, they can exhibit wave-like behaviour, which scientists have observed in experiments dating back over 200 years.**

Things you can see in everyday life can be described as having wave-like behaviour, such as ripples propagating in a pond, or particle-like behaviour, for example the football you kick around in the park with your friends. At the microscopic scale, very tiny particles – electrons, protons and photons – can exhibit behaviours we associate with both waves and particles, which leads to many weird (and useful) effects. This is commonly referred to as wave-particle duality, which is a key concept in the field of quantum mechanics (see page 68).

Imagine you are shining a torch at a screen with two narrows slits in it. If you place another screen behind the initial screen and observe the pattern of light that falls on it after travelling through the slits, what pattern of light do you think you will see? You might think it will be two narrow bands of light, but instead you will see multiple bands of light. The reason for this is that the particles of light (photons) are acting like waves and interfering with each other. Just like the waves in a pond mix and combine, photons passing through each slit of the screen are doing the same, leading to many bright bands being produced on the second screen due to this interference.

Throughout history many famous physicists and mathematicians have worked on theories surrounding wave-particle duality, including Albert Einstein with the photo-electric effect and Thomas Young, who first devised the double slit experiment.

In the 1920s, another physicist named Louis de Broglie aimed at mathematically describing the wave-like nature of particles – in particular the electron. In his PhD thesis, he formally came up with the de Broglie wave equation, which described how the electron exhibited wave-like properties. His theory now underpins many pieces of highly useful experimental equipment, such as the scanning electron microscope. The technology relies upon the wave-like nature of the electron, as described by wave-particle duality, to enable the technology to image very small objects (see page 60).

# INTERFERING WITH
# WAVE-PARTICLE DUALITY

When a beam of light passes through two slits in one screen, instinctively you would expect to see only two bright lines on a screen placed behind. However, because light particles exhibit wave-like properties, the two beams of light interfere with each other many times, resulting in multiple light and dark bands on the second panel.

# Can we be certain about the uncertainty principle?

**➡ The uncertainty principle states that the precise location and velocity of subatomic particles cannot be measured simultaneously.**

Published by German theoretical physicist Werner Heisenberg in 1927, the uncertainty principle is the subject of many puns and jokes. The actual principle is beautiful in its simplicity and is described by a single equation, which states that the behaviour of subatomic (quantum) particles is hard to predict precisely and has a level of uncertainty – hence the name.

The uncertainty principle postulates that we cannot measure both the position and the momentum of a particle with absolute precision. In other words, the more we know about one of these quantities, the less we know about the other. This is in stark contrast with what we experience in our large-scale view of the world, which is described by classical physics, where no such limitation on simultaneous measurements exists. The implications and consequences of the uncertainty principle are profound and far reaching.

However, the uncertainty principle was questioned in the 1990s by a group of physicists. The scientists performed the famous double slit experiment (see page 70), and showed that both a particle's position and velocity could be measured to high precision.

More recently, scientists have been testing this principle in new ways. In one, they took many small measurements – in order to interact with the experiment as little as possible – and stacked them together. When these separate values were stacked, they found that their measurements were more accurate than the uncertainty principle should allow them to be.

There is, however, an important distinction to be made here. Although it may not be the process of measuring values that introduces uncertainty, it is still not possible to know different quantum states simultaneously. So, for now anyway, the uncertainty principle still seems to hold true.

# SCHRÖDINGER'S QUANTUM CAT

Schrödinger's cat is often associated with the uncertainty principle and it's easy to see why. Originally, it was a thought experiment designed to illustrate one of the paradoxes of quantum mechanics. Devised in 1935, it describes a cat placed into a box with a radioactive element. The radioactive element can decay over time – when it does, it releases lethal radiation that kills the cat. Quantum mechanics states that we cannot know for certain the wellbeing of the cat. There is some probability that the creature is dead and some probability that it is alive. Without looking in the box, the cat can be thought of as both alive and dead at the same time.

# What's the antimatter?

→ It's the shadowy twin of ordinary matter. Understanding how antimatter differs from matter could unlock some of the deepest mysteries of the cosmos. Meanwhile, down here on Earth it already helps doctors to find tumours inside patients.

In 1928, British physicist Paul Dirac brought together quantum mechanics and special relativity in the Dirac Equation, sometimes called the most beautiful equation in physics. The equation provided a detailed description of how particles like electrons behave. It also predicted that the electron should have an antiparticle – a twin with exactly the same mass, but an opposite charge.

This seemed like a fanciful idea until a positive electron, or positron, was discovered just a few years later. Antiprotons followed in 1955, and since then scientists have found a whole menagerie of antiparticles. They've even combined antiprotons with positrons to make anti-hydrogen atoms.

Antimatter is tricky stuff, though. When an antiparticle collides with its particle, they annihilate in a huge burst of energy. With just a soup can full of antimatter, you could unleash more energy than a big power station generates in a year.

Fortunately for us, there aren't great clumps of antimatter lurking in our universe. But theory suggests that the Big Bang (see page 14) should have created equal amounts of matter and antimatter, which leads to one of the biggest mysteries in physics. Given their equal-yet-opposite nature, why is there so much more matter than antimatter today? It hints at a fundamental difference between matter and antimatter – a potentially minuscule bias that remains hidden from physicists.

Antimatter may be exotic, but there are bits of it all around us, albeit briefly. For example, some forms of radioactive decay (see page 18) spit out a positron, which can be used in a medical imaging procedure called positron emission tomography (PET). Patients are injected with molecules that carry a radioactive isotope to specific parts of the body. The isotope produces positrons that immediately annihilate with electrons inside the patient, generating gamma rays. The PET scanner detects these gamma rays, allowing doctors to pinpoint tumours inside the patient.

Tiny amounts of antimatter are being produced in your fruit bowl, too. Bananas contain lots of potassium atoms, a few of which are radioactive isotopes that occasionally pop out a positron – roughly once every 75 minutes or so.

# THE SHADOW WORLD

## MATTER

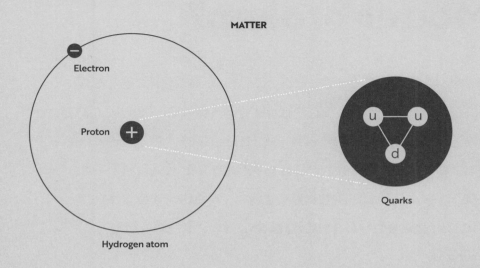

Electron

Proton

Quarks

u   u

d

Hydrogen atom

## ANTIMATTER

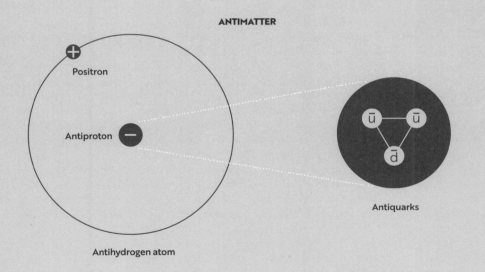

Positron

Antiproton

Antiquarks

ū   ū

d̄

Antihydrogen atom

A hydrogen atom is made of a proton and an electron. Protons contain even smaller particles called quarks, which come in flavours such as 'up' and 'down'. Hydrogen's antimatter twin is anti-hydrogen, made from a positron (a positive electron) and an antiproton containing the corresponding antiquarks. Scientists are studying the differences between hydrogen and anti-hydrogen to test some of the most fundamental rules in physics. But these are tricky experiments because when matter meets antimatter their mass is instantly converted into energy, according to Einstein's famous $E=mc^2$ equation.

# Is the Standard Model broken?

**⟶ It's not broken, but it might need updating. The Standard Model has long provided a way for scientists to describe the particles in our universe. But there are new discoveries that need to be incorporated, including dark matter.**

First developed in the 1970s, the Standard Model provides a way to relate three of the four fundamental forces – electromagnetism and the strong and weak nuclear forces – with the basic building blocks (particles) of our universe. It categorises these particles, based on their various properties, into a number of families. The elementary particles are fermions (electrons and quarks), which make up matter, and bosons (like photons), which carry forces.

Since its inception, the Standard Model has been subject to a lot of probing to test how well it stands up. We now know that there are aspects missing from the Standard Model and things that it cannot account for, including the magnetism of the muon, the slight dominance of matter over antimatter and both dark matter and dark energy.

The muon, for example, is a massive, unstable relative of the electron, which is one of the fundamental particles of the Standard Model. Scientists have recently been able to make extremely accurate measurements of the muon's internal magnetism, which reflects how the muon interacts with forces and other particles, and have found that this magnetism deviates (albeit by a small amount) from predictions according to the Standard Model.

Another problem with the Standard Model is that is does not include the final fundamental force of gravity. Scientists have yet to find a particle that describes how gravity 'communicates' with other particles.

The Standard Model also neglects dark matter and dark energy, which make up the vast majority of our universe; indeed, it can only explain about 5 per cent of the energy present. There is much uncertainty around both, but one favoured candidate for dark matter (albeit one of numerous theories) is the neutrino (see page 78).

So, like many things in science, the Standard Model is certainly useful and provides a valuable starting point, but it has limitations. And there will no doubt be further discrepancies in the future as scientists achieve increasingly more accurate measurements of the universe.

# MISSING PIECES

The Standard Model of particle physics is an intricate puzzle that scientists have spent decades putting together. It has been tremendously successful in explaining many aspects of subatomic particles and predicted the existence of the Higgs boson (page 80), for example. But it's missing some pieces, including gravity, dark matter and dark energy, and it's far from clear how to make them fit. Some scientists want to expand the model to include lots of extra 'supersymmetric' particles, while others think the whole model should be replaced by one based not on particles, but on tiny vibrating one-dimensional 'strings'.

# What flavour is a neutrino?

→ **Neutrinos come in three elusive flavours. Each neutrino leaves a signature trail, which scientists can unravel to predict which particle caused it.**

All matter around you is made of fundamental particles. These are the basic building blocks of everything you see in the world. Physicists group these fundamental particles into something known as the Standard Model. One intriguing and mysterious group of particles within the Standard Model are known as neutrinos, and they come in three slightly different flavours: the electron neutrino, muon neutrino and tau neutrino. Intriguingly, they can swap, or oscillate, between each flavour (or type) at will.

Distinguishing between the different types of neutrino is very tricky, as each particle has a tiny mass and no electric charge, and barely interacts with matter. Indeed, they interact so little that as you are reading this, approximately 100 billion neutrinos produced in the Sun are passing through your fingernail.

So, how do physicists prove that they exist? To test their theories, physicists needed to design experiments to detect and capture neutrinos. As neutrinos interact very infrequently with matter, when they do interact you need to be ready. Trying to detect a neutrino interaction on the surface

of the Earth would be difficult, as there are simply too many other particles and sources of radiation. To counteract this, scientists build huge particle detectors deep underground to shield them from unwanted particles. One such example is Super-Kamiokande in Japan, buried over 1,000 metres deep in an old, abandoned mine. The facility contains a 40-metre tank containing over 50,000 tons of ultra-pure water, surrounded by ultra-sensitive light detectors. Scientists wait for different types of neutrinos to interact with the water, studying the radiation and particles produced after the interaction.

Super-Kamiokande was the first detector to provide evidence of the elusive neutrino oscillation in 1998. In 2015, Takaaki Kajita and Arthur McDonald won the Nobel Prize for their work confirming the detection of neutrino oscillations. Due to the success of Super-Kamiokande, a significantly larger version of the detector is currently under construction: Hyper-Kamiokande. Nicknamed Hyper-K, the detector will contain over 1 billion litres of ultra-pure water and will hunt for other elusive particle interactions such as proton decays.

# HUNTING FOR NEUTRINO OSCILLATIONS

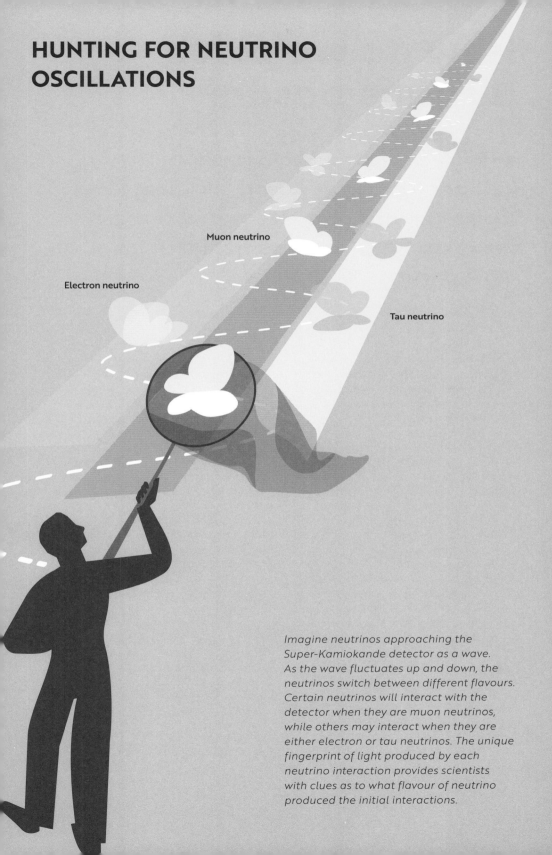

Muon neutrino

Electron neutrino

Tau neutrino

Imagine neutrinos approaching the Super-Kamiokande detector as a wave. As the wave fluctuates up and down, the neutrinos switch between different flavours. Certain neutrinos will interact with the detector when they are muon neutrinos, while others may interact when they are either electron or tau neutrinos. The unique fingerprint of light produced by each neutrino interaction provides scientists with clues as to what flavour of neutrino produced the initial interactions.

# How do we catch a Higgs boson?

**→ Try using the Large Hadron Collider. The Higgs boson, nicknamed 'God's particle', was discovered there in the Higgs field – a force field that gives most particles their mass.**

Why does so much of the stuff in our universe have mass, while other things, such as light, have no mass at all? The answer lies in an invisible force field and a particle now famously called the Higgs boson.

Nature is governed by four fundamental forces: gravity, the strong nuclear force, the weak nuclear force and electromagnetism. Each force is carried by a type of particle known as a boson. The W and Z bosons that carry the weak force are very similar to the particles of light, called photons, which carry electromagnetism.

However, scientists couldn't understand why W and Z bosons are relatively heavy particles, whereas photons have zero mass. In the 1960s, several physicists tried to explain this by proposing a new kind of force field that gives W and Z bosons mass, while leaving photons alone. It was named the Higgs field, after physicist Peter Higgs. The more a particle interacts with this field, the heavier it becomes.

The Higgs boson is a kind of ripple in the Higgs field. Proponents thought that it could be the last missing piece in the Standard Model, the menagerie of particles and forces that make up the basic building blocks of the universe (see page 76).

To hunt for their divine quarry, physicists built the Large Hadron Collider (LHC) at CERN, near Geneva. This vast machine smashes protons together to make a high-energy soup of exotic particles. After several years of sifting through this debris, CERN scientists announced in 2012 that they had good evidence that these collisions had created Higgs bosons, confirming the existence of the omnipresent Higgs field. For their prescient predictions, Peter Higgs and François Englert won the Nobel Prize in Physics in 2013.

So is our understanding of particle physics now complete? Not a bit of it – there is still plenty of weird stuff that the Standard Model cannot explain, including such mysteries as dark matter and dark energy.

# THE HIGGS FIELD

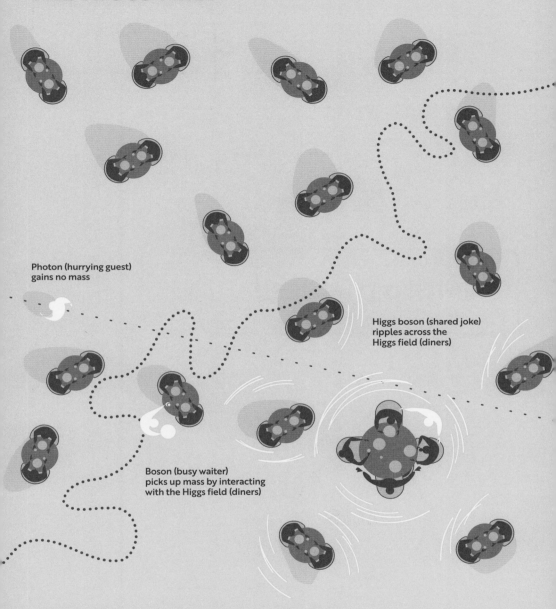

**Photon (hurrying guest) gains no mass**

**Higgs boson (shared joke) ripples across the Higgs field (diners)**

**Boson (busy waiter) picks up mass by interacting with the Higgs field (diners)**

*If the Higgs field is a restaurant packed with diners, a guest hurrying through the restaurant represents a photon particle passing through the Higgs field quickly without any interaction. Meanwhile, a busy waiter stopping at tables to pick up plates and glasses represents a boson particle passing through the field slowly gaining mass. Both particles start with zero mass and mass is only gained by interaction with the Higgs field, so only the boson (the busy waiter) picks up mass. Meanwhile, the guests on one table share a joke. Other guests rush over to hear it, then return to their tables to share the joke, creating a ripple that spreads across the room. This ripple, which can also be imagined as the bump created when you flick the end of a rope, is analogous to the Higgs boson.*

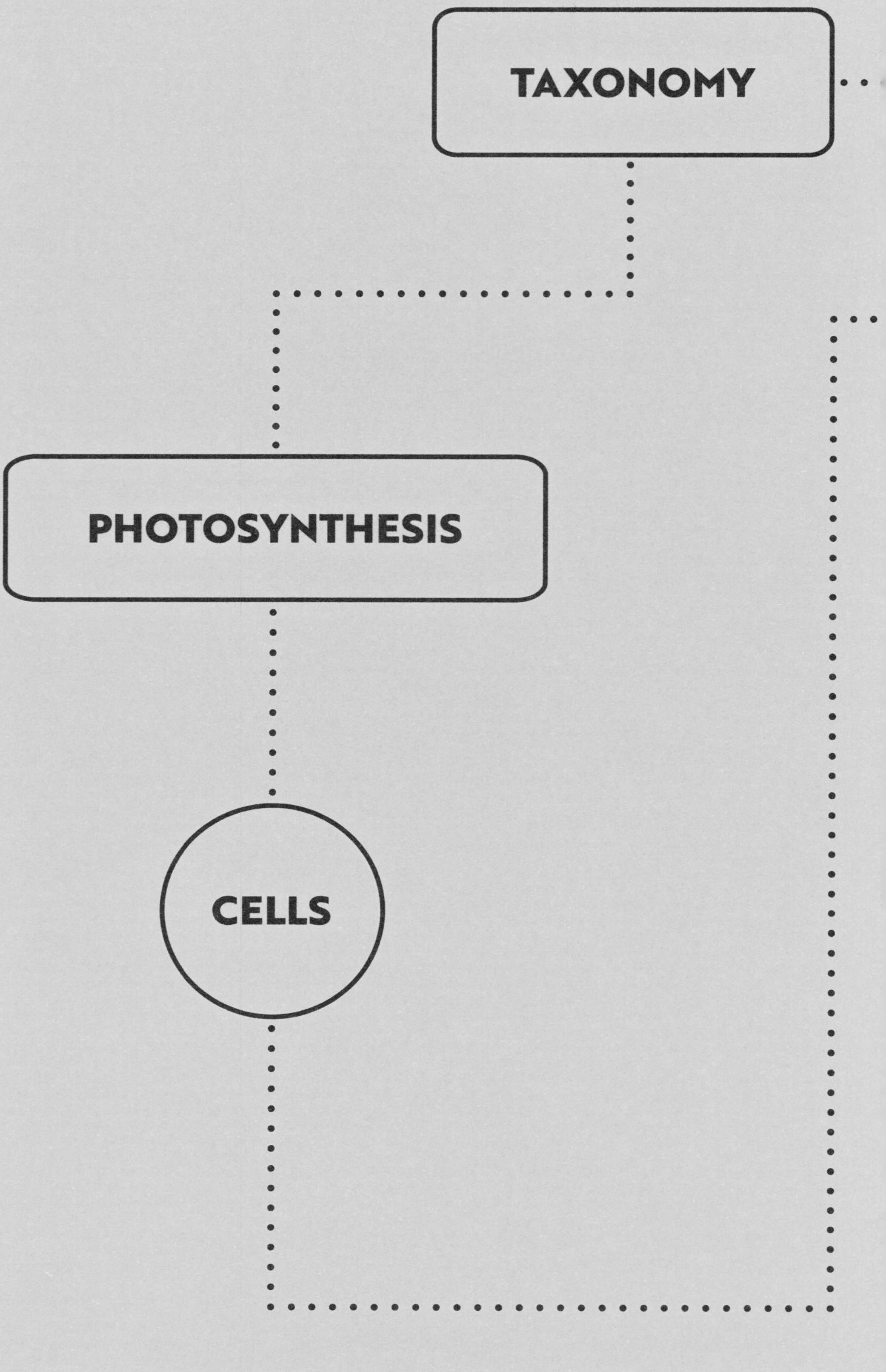

TAXONOMY

PHOTOSYNTHESIS

CELLS

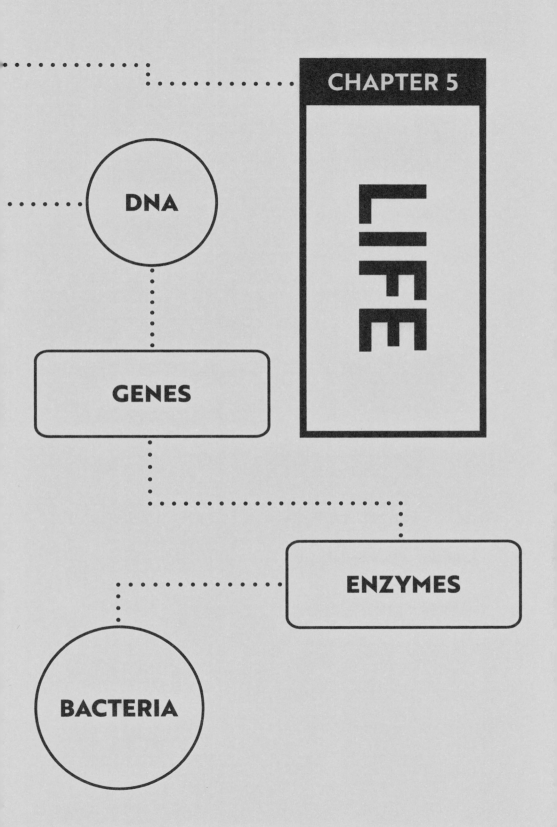

CHAPTER 5

LIFE

DNA

GENES

ENZYMES

BACTERIA

# INTRODUCTION

Science may not be able to tell you much about the meaning of life, but it can offer stunning insights about life on Earth and the processes that drive it.

To explore the glorious variety of life around us, it helps to have a map. That's exactly what Carl Linnaeus provided when he developed the first modern system for sorting animals and plants into distinct groups. This marked the beginning of **TAXONOMY**, the science of naming and classifying organisms (see page 88).

Linnaeus based his taxonomy on the physical characteristics of each organism and gave each organism a unique Latin name to indicate its place in this grand scheme. These days, taxonomy is guided by studying the genetic make-up of organisms, which reveals how they relate to one another.

Almost all of these life forms ultimately get the energy they need from the Sun, harvested through a process called **PHOTOSYNTHESIS** (see page 90). Plants, algae and some bacteria use light to combine water and carbon dioxide to make glucose and oxygen. When we eat plants, we harvest the solar energy that was locked into glucose and then use oxygen to help digest it.

These biochemical miracles all happen inside **CELLS**, the basic structural unit of all living things (see page 92). Cells were first glimpsed under 17th-century microscopes.

Many organisms make do with just a single cell – in contrast, humans are built from trillions of cells, of many different types, which all have specific functions.

Once scientists delved inside cells, they found that these squishy bags contained a seething mass of molecules, all engaged in the biochemical reactions that make things alive. Perhaps the most iconic of these molecules is deoxyribonucleic acid – better known as **DNA** . It's double-helix structure contains a chemical code with all the information needed to create an organism (see page 94).

**GENES** are short sections of DNA that provide cells with the instructions for making useful molecules. For example, some genes carry the codes for **ENZYMES**, which are special types of protein that speed up chemical reactions in our cells (see page 98). Without enzymes, life would slow to a crawl and basic tasks such as digestion and movement would be impossible.

Figuring out how DNA stores and transmits these biological blueprints has guided scientists to understand the origins of many diseases, which can potentially help to treat them. It also enables scientists to alter the genetic codes of organisms such as **BACTERIA**, giving them extraordinary abilities that can be harnessed to produce fuels or medicines. By looking deep within the processes that allow life to flourish, science is now using that knowledge to help sustain our own lives.

# LIFE MAP

## GENETICS

### ENZYME
Special type of protein that acts as a biological catalyst, speeding up a chemical reaction without undergoing any permanent change itself.

### ALLELE
Variant form of a gene. One copy of each gene is inherited from each parent – if they differ and one allele is 'dominant', that physical trait will 'win', such as brown eyes over blue. This includes our risk of disease and allergies.

### PROTEINS
Large, complex molecules made up of amino acids that perform a range of critical functions within organisms – essential for the structure, function and regulation of human tissues and organs.

### GENE
Basic unit of heredity passed from parent to child, comprising sections of DNA that provide cells with instructions for a physical characteristic or function.

### AMINO ACID
Small building block that makes up proteins – there are twenty different types in the human body.

### RIBOSOME
Found in all cells, it links together amino acids to form proteins using the code from a type of RNA called messenger RNA.

### DNA
Deoxyribonucleic acid – an organic chemical that holds instructions for making proteins in an organism. Each molecule has a double-helix structure.

### ROSALIND FRANKLIN
British chemist (1920–58) who produced detailed X-ray diffraction images of DNA, which contributed to the discovery of its double-helix structure.

### JAMES WATSON AND FRANCIS CRICK
Scientists who determined the double-helix structure of DNA molecules in 1953, sharing the Nobel Prize for Medicine for the discovery with colleague Maurice Wilkins.

# BIOLOGY

## MUTATION
Change in the genetic sequence of an organism, either by mistake when copied or due to environmental factors.

## DIRECTED EVOLUTION
Making repeated changes to the DNA code for a protein, in order to enhance a desired property in that protein.

## GENOME
Complete genetic code or set of DNA instructions that contains all the genetic information of an organism.

## GENE SEQUENCING
Process for determining the order of bases in DNA molecules. Helps with biological and medical research and diagnosis.

## BASE PAIR
Each strand forming the DNA double helix is formed of small molecules, known as bases, which pair up to stick the two strands together.

## CELL
Basic building block of all living things and the smallest unit that can live on its own. Usually made up of a membrane, nucleus and cytoplasm.

## BACTERIA
Microscopic single-celled, or simple, organisms found everywhere on Earth, including inside other organisms. May be either helpful or harmful to humans.

## EUKARYA
Complex organisms (as opposed to single-celled ones) with cells containing nuclei bounded by membranes. Includes people and plants.

## ARCHAEA
Type of primitive, single-celled organism lacking a defined nucleus; similar to bacteria but with some unique characteristics.

## PHOTOSYNTHESIS
Chemical process by which plants grow. Energy from sunlight is absorbed by a pigment called chlorophyll, and used to combine water with carbon dioxide to make glucose and oxygen.

## TAXONOMY
System first devised by Carl Linnaeus for classifying living organisms by dividing them into categories, progressively subdivided into smaller and smaller groups.

# Is taxonomy just name calling?

⟶ **Sticks and stones may well break bones, but names are incredibly useful when it comes to categorising the inter-relatedness of life on Earth. This makes taxonomy – the science of naming, describing and classifying organisms – very important indeed.**

If you like living things and enjoy organising them, then you'll love taxonomy. Carl Linnaeus certainly did. In the 18th century, the Swedish biologist, who became known as the 'father of modern taxonomy', came up with the first modern system for classifying organisms. The Linnaean system divides life into broad categories and then subdivides them into progressively smaller and smaller groups. It's like zooming in from a particular country to a city, then to a street and down to a house, and finally to a person.

He also created the binomial system of naming species, which uses two Latin words to denote an organism's genus and species. Humans, for example, are *Homo sapiens*. He used the system to name over 12,000 species of plants and animals, and the method is still in use today.

Over time, as scientists continue to learn more about the natural world and develop new methods to study it, Linnaeus' original ideas have been refined. All life can now be subdivided into domains, kingdoms, phyla, classes, orders, families, genera and species. In 1977, American microbiologist Carl Woese pioneered the technique of phylogenetic taxonomy, which uses the genetic differences that exist between organisms in order to classify them.

As a result, the predominant view today is that life is split into three domains: eukarya, bacteria and archaea. Woese recognised and classified archaea, which are a type of primitive, single-celled organism. Bacteria are also single-celled, while eukaryotes, such as people and plants, tend to be more complex and have cells that contain nuclei bounded by membranes.

It's now comparatively easy to isolate and study genetic material such as DNA, and as a result, scientists are continually tweaking the classification of certain organisms. Red pandas, for example, are now classified as part of the raccoon family, while giant pandas belong to the bear family. The phylogenetic tree of life just keeps on getting more interesting!

# THE TREE OF LIFE

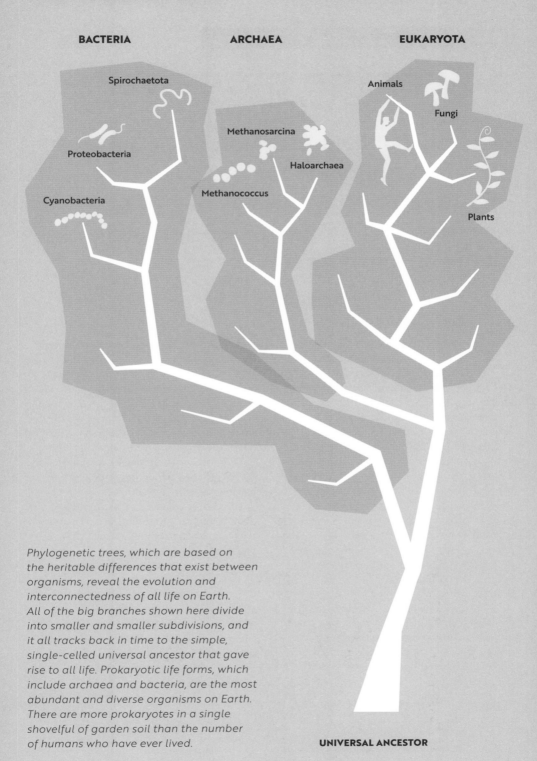

**BACTERIA**

Spirochaetota

Proteobacteria

Cyanobacteria

**ARCHAEA**

Methanosarcina

Haloarchaea

Methanococcus

**EUKARYOTA**

Animals

Fungi

Plants

*Phylogenetic trees, which are based on the heritable differences that exist between organisms, reveal the evolution and interconnectedness of all life on Earth. All of the big branches shown here divide into smaller and smaller subdivisions, and it all tracks back in time to the simple, single-celled universal ancestor that gave rise to all life. Prokaryotic life forms, which include archaea and bacteria, are the most abundant and diverse organisms on Earth. There are more prokaryotes in a single shovelful of garden soil than the number of humans who have ever lived.*

**UNIVERSAL ANCESTOR**

# How does photosynthesis power the planet?

**→ A ray of light, a breath of air, a droplet of water – these are the ingredients of photosynthesis, a series of chemical reactions that has sustained virtually all life on Earth for billions of years.**

People once thought that plants grew larger by converting soil into stems and leaves. In the 17th century, Jan Baptist van Helmont performed an iconic experiment to prove this wasn't true. He carefully weighed a willow sapling and some soil, and put them both in a pot. For five long years he watered the tree and watched it grow, making sure that no other material fell into the soil. Finally, he took the tree out of the pot, shook off all the soil and weighed them both. The tree had grown much larger, but the soil had lost almost none of its weight.

That's because the tree built its branches, roots and leaves from water and air, using a process called photosynthesis – arguably the most important chemical process on the planet.

Plants use a pigment called chlorophyll that absorbs red light and channels its energy into reactions that combine water with carbon dioxide from the air. This produces a ring-shaped molecule called glucose – the main sugar found in your blood – along with

oxygen, which is released back into the air. The plant uses glucose as a building block to make all sorts of carbohydrate molecules, including cellulose and starch. Cellulose is a stiff polymer that strengthens the plant's cell walls, helping it to grow. Starch acts as the plant's battery, storing the sun's energy in its chemical bonds. When we eat plants, or the animals that feed on them, we are consuming carbon and gleaning energy that was first captured by photosynthesis.

The oxygen released by photosynthesis comes in pretty handy, too. Every breath we take grabs oxygen from the air, which we use to burn up our food to release its energy. Without photosynthesis, we'd be toast. (Spoiler: there wouldn't be any toast, either.)

Even fossil fuels owe their energy to photosynthesis. When dead plants are crushed and heated for aeons beneath accumulating layers of rocks, they form coal. Burning coal releases energy that ancient plants captured from sunlight hundreds of millions of years ago.

# POWER PLANTS

Around the world, photosynthesis converts about 200 billion tonnes of carbon dioxide into sugars every year. That's over 6,000 tonnes of carbon dioxide every single second – enough to fill a balloon bigger than Egypt's Great Pyramid of Giza.

Photosynthesis also harvests vast amounts of sunlight. In just two minutes, photosynthesis gathers the same amount of energy carried by all the oil in a large supertanker: 12,000 trillion joules.

# Are cells the key to life?

**→ Well, you wouldn't be reading this without them! All living things are made of cells – and you are no exception. Your body is made of around 40 trillion cells, all working away to keep you going. Cells aren't just the key to life – cells are life.**

The cell is the basic structural and functional unit of life. Cells are tiny little 'bags of stuff'; however, they're mostly far too small to be seen with the human eye, so scientists had to wait for the invention of the microscope before they could be discovered. That moment came in 1665, when English scientist Robert Hooke peered through a microscope's eyepiece and saw a plant cell. He detailed his revelation in his book *Micrographia* and called the structure a cell, because it reminded him of the small rooms lived in by monks.

Not long afterwards, Dutch scientist Antonie van Leeuwenhoek developed microscope lenses that were more powerful and used them to detect other minuscule entities, including bacteria and spermatozoa.

It was becoming clear that single-celled organisms existed and that larger, more complex organisms were also made from cells. The idea was formalised in 1839 by Theodor Schwann and Matthias Schleiden, who proposed that cells are the fundamental units of both plants and animals. This became known as cell theory. The idea was further expanded in 1855 by Rudolf Virchow, who stated that all cells are generated from existing cells. They can't just 'pop up' from nowhere.

It's an evolutionary conundrum. If all life on Earth can be traced back to an initial, single-celled ancestor, how did that first cell come to be? Some think the small molecules that led to life were created at deep-sea vents or carried to Earth on meteorites. No one knows for sure, but the first cells, and therefore the first life on Earth, emerged around 3.8 billion years ago. From that day to this, there has been an unbroken chain of cells – from that first single-celled organism right through to us, and all the life that exists on Earth today.

# THE BUILDING BLOCK OF LIFE

All multicellular things, such as humans, dinosaurs, fish and plants, are (or were, in the case of dinosaurs) made up of lots of cells of different kinds. There are, for example, muscle cells, nerve cells and fat cells. Each cell type is specialised and performs a particular function, yet they all fit together to create a whole that is so much more than the sum of its parts. Working together, cells give us the ability to live, think and do. They provide the essence of being alive.

# What can we find in our DNA?

→ DNA's spiralling double helix carries the secret code of life, written in a chemical language. The code is 3 billion letters long and contains a series of spectacular recipes for building the biological molecules in our bodies.

The instructions for building a living creature are written in its genes. Scientists studied genetics for decades before they figured out what genes are actually made of. By the 1940s, there was growing evidence that genetic information is carried by a molecule called deoxyribonucleic acid (DNA). But even then, scientists weren't sure what molecules of DNA looked like.

In 1953, James Watson and Francis Crick cracked the problem, building on the work of many other scientists – not least Rosalind Franklin, who gathered the crucial data. By studying the patterns created when X-rays scattered through a crystal of DNA, they realised that two long strands of DNA twist around one another to form a double helix.

Each strand carries a series of small molecules called adenine (A), guanine (G), thymine (T) and cytosine (C), collectively known as bases. These bases can pair up to stick the two DNA strands together – T hooks up with A, while C clings to G. Discovering this structure allowed scientists to understand how DNA works.

If DNA's bases are like letters, then genes are long sentences. One of their main jobs is to store recipes for making proteins, which do a lot of the biochemical tasks in our bodies. Proteins are made from hundreds of small building blocks called amino acids, available in twenty different varieties.

The sequence of DNA bases tells the body which amino acids to use as it builds a new protein. Here's how it works. A special protein called an enzyme (see page 98) unzips the double helix, so that its code can be copied and carried to a tiny piece of biological machinery called a ribosome. As the ribosome reads the code it builds up a protein, one amino acid at a time.

If the DNA code contains errors – the wrong base in the wrong place, for example – it can sometimes increase the risk of cancer, diabetes and various other conditions. Medical researchers often use a technique called DNA sequencing to read the genetic code in order to diagnose diseases and understand their causes.

# DNA STRUCTURE

Human DNA carries about 3 billion pairs of bases, of which just a few per cent spell out our 21,000 or so genes. If you stretched your DNA out into a straight line, the DNA from a single cell would be about two metres long. To fit DNA inside a cell, it is carefully wrapped around scaffold proteins called histones, then coiled and coiled again to form structures called chromosomes. In humans, 46 of these chromosomes pack into the cell nucleus, which is barely six micrometres wide – 200 times smaller than a grain of sand.

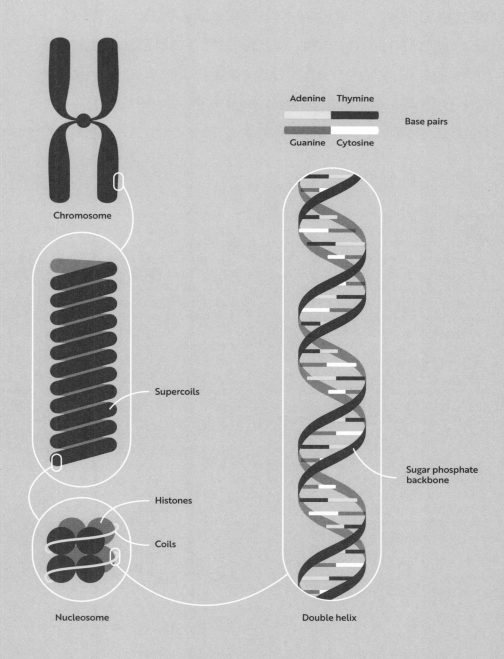

Chromosome

Adenine    Thymine

Guanine    Cytosine

Base pairs

Supercoils

Sugar phosphate backbone

Histones

Coils

Nucleosome

Double helix

# How do we sequence a gene?

⟶ If you're a geneticist, the answer is 'with ease'. It's now relatively cheap and straightforward to sequence or decode the DNA found inside cells. This is helping scientists to fathom how life develops, understand illness and devise new therapies.

Genes are short sections of DNA. Humans have around 21,000 different genes. Fruit flies have around 14,000, whereas rice has about 51,000 genes. Each gene provides the cells inside living things with a set of instructions for making something useful, like a protein. Working together, they influence everything from height to hair colour, and from disease to personality.

When the Augustinian friar Gregor Mendel was studying pea plants back in the 19th century, he realised that characteristics such as flower colour and seed shape were determined by 'units of inheritance' that are passed from parent to offspring. We now know these units are genes and that his pea plants turned out the way they did because they were inheriting different versions, or alleles, of particular genes. If an allele is dominant, then only one copy is needed to have an effect, but if an allele is recessive, two copies are required.

Genes only became known after DNA was discovered and its structure was deciphered. In 1952, Rosalind Franklin and Raymond Gosling took an X-ray photograph of DNA that led James Watson and Francis Crick to propose that the structure of DNA is like a twisted ladder or double helix.

The 'rungs' are made of pairs of chemicals called nucleotides; although there are only four different nucleotides, an organism's full genetic code or 'genome' can be many billions of nucleotides long.

Genes themselves vary in size, from thousands to millions of pairs of nucleotides, and a gene's sequence is simply the order in which these nucleotides appear. It's now possible to swab the inside of your cheek, send the sample off to a sequencing company and then learn about the specific versions of key genes that you carry. This can help to shed light on your ancestry and also your risk of developing certain diseases.

# DNA SEQUENCING

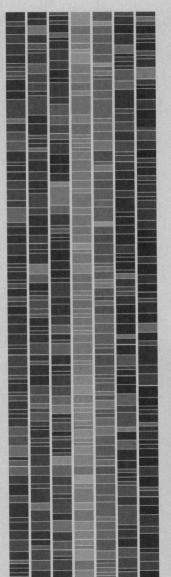

DNA sequencing is the method that is used to determine the order or 'sequence' of nucleotides in DNA. The method has become quicker and cheaper over the years, and now 'high-throughput sequencing' can be used to determine not just the sequence of a gene, but the sequence of a whole genome in as little as a day. Surprising insights are revealed when the genomes of different organisms are compared. Rice plants, for example, have about 30,000 more genes than we do!

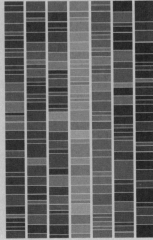

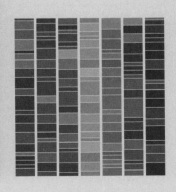

**RICE**
c. 51,000 genes

**HUMANS**
c. 21,000 genes

**FRUIT FLIES**
c. 14,000 genes

# How do we evolve an enzyme?

⟶ **Enzymes are nature's catalysts, speeding up vital chemical reactions in our bodies. Scientists can now evolve enzymes in the lab, giving them a turbo boost so that they produce medicine or fuels, or perform a host of other useful tasks.**

An enzyme is a special type of protein that speeds up a chemical reaction – it is a biological catalyst. Unlike many human-made catalysts, enzymes can perform these reactions without needing lots of heat or pressure, and they can make reactions run trillions of times faster than normal. The most crucial processes of life – from digesting food to flexing our muscles – all depend on enzymes.

Enzymes, like all proteins, are built from hundreds of amino acid building blocks. Thousands of different enzymes are contained in our bodies, each with a specialised function. Enzymes often work in teams to perform a series of chemical reactions, such as those involved in generating energy from carbohydrates. These reactions happen in a specific part of the enzyme, known as its active site. Many medicines are designed to block an enzyme's active site, dialling down unwanted biological activity.

If an error creeps into an enzyme's DNA blueprint, it can sometimes put the wrong amino acid in a crucial part of the active site. This sometimes makes the enzyme less effective, but occasionally the error makes it a better catalyst, or even alters which chemical reaction it catalyses.

Scientists have learned how to speed up this kind of 'enzyme evolution' in a test tube, potentially giving the enzyme supercharged abilities. American scientist Frances Arnold shared the 2018 Nobel Prize in Chemistry for pioneering this approach, which is called directed evolution.

First, she introduces some random errors into the DNA that carries the code for a particular enzyme. Then she pops that DNA inside helpful bacteria, which start to make lots of mutated enzymes. After testing how effective these enzymes are, the winners are taken through to a second round of mutation and testing; then a third round, and a fourth, and so on until a champion enzyme emerges.

This strategy has helped scientists harness the power of enzymes for a variety of everyday tasks. Enzymes in laundry detergent help to wash your whites whiter, while others help to produce medicines, or transform the tough stems of plants into renewable fuels.

# THE POWER OF ENZYMES

Enzymes are specially shaped with a tiny chemical reactor on their surface. This 'active site' is lined with chemical groups in just the right positions to catch smaller molecules and convert them into something else. Scientists initially thought that an incoming molecule (or 'substrate') fits into the active site like a key fits into a lock. That's true, up to a point, but flexible enzymes can also change shape to enclose the molecule, moulding into the ideal form for their work.

**Molecule enters the enzyme's active site.**

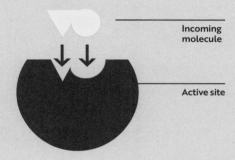

Incoming molecule

Active site

**Enzyme binds the molecule.**

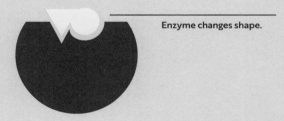

Enzyme changes shape.

**Enzyme triggers a reaction.**

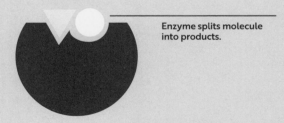

Enzyme splits molecule into products.

**Products leave the enzyme's active site.**

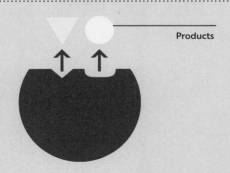

Products

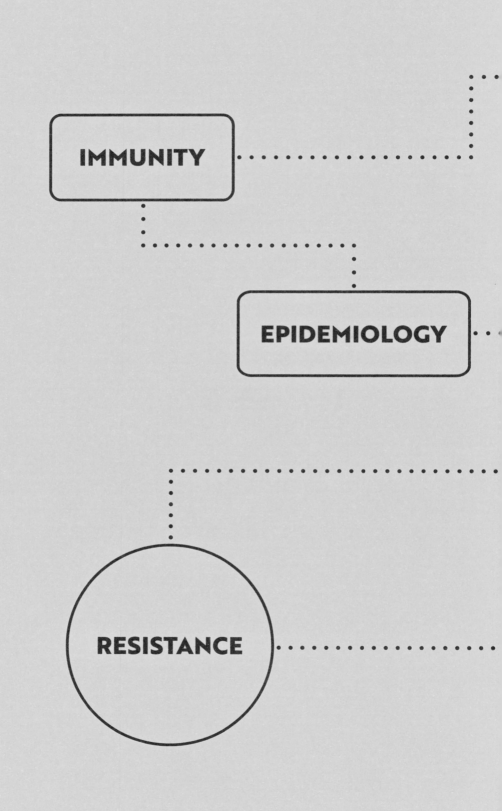

GERMS

PENICILLIN

GENE
EDITING

# CHAPTER 6

# HEALTH

# INTRODUCTION

**S**tudying the processes of life has transformed our understanding of biology and led to remarkable improvements in our health. By identifying the causes of disease, scientists have developed an arsenal of effective medicines and found ways to prevent people from contracting infections. More recently, researchers have begun to tackle diseases by tweaking the fundamentals of life, through reprogramming our cells and editing our genetic code.

One of the foundational moments in preventative medicine occurred in the 19th century. Hungarian doctor Ignaz Semmelweis realised that if doctors washed their hands before treating new mothers in a maternity ward, they could prevent the women from contracting fatal 'childbed fever'.

This is because many diseases are carried from one person to another by **GERMS**, such as bacteria and viruses (see page 106). We now kill germs using processes such as **PASTEURISATION** and sterilisation, and give people vaccines to stimulate their **IMMUNITY** to germs (see page 108).

Also in the 19th century, scientists began to track the spread of diseases such as cholera. This led to the science of **EPIDEMIOLOGY**, which studies the occurrence of diseases in populations (see page 110). It provides vital information about how to stop the transmission of infections such as COVID-19. Researchers can also use epidemiology to identify who might be most vulnerable to a particular disease.

Using soap and water is often enough to kill the bacteria lurking on a surface, but these microbes are much harder to eliminate once they proliferate inside a patient's body. So the discovery of the powerful antibiotic **PENICILLIN** in 1928 marked a key turning point in healthcare. For the first time, doctors had a really effective treatment that could prevent and cure a wide range of bacterial infections (see page 112).

Over time, though, bacteria can evolve to resist the full range of antibiotics at our disposal and become 'superbugs'. The rise of antibacterial **RESISTANCE** means that a growing number of infections are becoming harder to treat and scientists are racing to find new types of antibiotics to counter this threat.

Many diseases emerge from faults in our own bodies, rather than germs. Scientists are now using cellular reprogramming to create replacement tissue as a treatment for conditions such as Parkinson's disease. This involves transforming healthy cells into a more youthful state called **STEM CELLS**, which can then be coaxed to grow into the specific type of cell needed by the patient (see page 114).

Another technique, called **GENE EDITING**, could even enable doctors to fix disease-causing problems deep in our DNA code (see page 116). This is already being used experimentally in patients to switch off genes involved in genetic disorders, such as sickle cell disease. It's just one example of how fundamental advances in biology are shaping healthcare more quickly than ever before.

# HEALTH MAP

## DISEASE

**FLORENCE NIGHTINGALE**
Nurse, social reformer and statistician (1820–1910), regarded as the founder of modern nursing; established the importance of sanitation in hospitals.

**EPIDEMIOLOGY**
The study of how often diseases occur in different groups of people and why.

**PANDEMIC**
Outbreak of an infectious disease that spreads quickly (epidemic) across a large geographical area.

**GERM**
Any microorganism, such as a bacterium, virus, fungus or protozoan, that causes disease.

**PASTEURISATION**
Germ-killing process for foods and drinks using heat; named after French scientist Louis Pasteur.

**IMMUNITY**
An organism's ability to resist disease and harmful substances, such as germs and toxins. May be innate or acquired.

**ANTIGEN**
Substance that causes the immune system to produce antibodies against it to minimise or prevent an illness, disease or allergic response.

**ANTIBODY**
Protective protein produced by the body's immune system to remove antigens. Also called immunoglobulin.

# MEDICINE

**PENCILLIN**
The first known widely effective antibiotic substance, discovered by Alexander Fleming in 1928.

**RESISTANCE**
When the bacteria or fungi that cause an infection no longer respond to treatment by the drugs designed to kill them.

**CELLULAR REPROGRAMMING**
Process of turning mature, specialised adult cells into stem cells, which can then be coaxed to become any cell of choice.

**STEM CELL**
Versatile, intermediate type of cell in the body that can develop into many other types of specialised cells.

**GERMLINE**
Population of reproductive cells that pass genomes to the next generation.

**CRISPR GENE EDITING**
Technology used to edit genes in plants and animals by altering a piece of DNA, or to turn genes on or off.

**CLONING**
Production of one or more genetically identical copies of a cell or organism by natural or artificial means.

# GENE THERAPY

# What's the idea of a germ?

⟶ Any infection-causing microscopic organism is a 'germ', including bacteria, viruses and fungi. They can infect living things, including animals and plants, and the diseases they cause range from the trivial to the life-threatening.

The 19th century was not a great time to have a baby. Back then, when Hungarian doctor Ignaz Semmelweis worked in an Austrian maternity ward, many mothers died from 'childbed fever' shortly after giving birth.

Semmelweis noticed that mothers who were looked after by midwives were less likely to die than those attended by doctors and medical students. The reason, he suggested, was that doctors and students went straight from dissecting corpses to delivering babies *without* washing their hands, and that they were somehow transferring the cause of the disease. The medics began to practice routine handwashing and the number of deaths declined soon after. It was the start of preventative medicine.

A few years later, French scientist Louis Pasteur was the first to show that germs cause disease. He developed vaccines against anthrax and rabies, and pioneered the germ-killing process of pasteurisation. However, it was a German scientist, Robert Koch, who developed Pasteur's ideas. Koch discovered the bacteria responsible for anthrax, tuberculosis and cholera, and the methods he pioneered enabled others to discover more types of disease-causing bacteria.

Germ theory – the idea that germs can cause disease – was gaining prominence, and in the 1870s, British surgeon Joseph Lister applied the theory to the operating theatre. He used phenol to sterilise surgical instruments, the patient's skin and the surgeon's hands and, as a result, the number of post-operative infections fell.

Germ theory is now widely accepted and the technique of sterilisation saves lives every day. Antiviral drugs help to ease the symptoms and curb the spread of viral infections. Antimicrobial drugs, such as antibiotics, help to treat bacterial infections (see page 112), while vaccines boost the immune system to keep diseases at bay (see page 108). Thanks to germ theory, many diseases that used to kill with impunity can now be treated with relative ease, and the global public health movement has never been as well equipped as it is today.

# THE WAR AGAINST GERMS

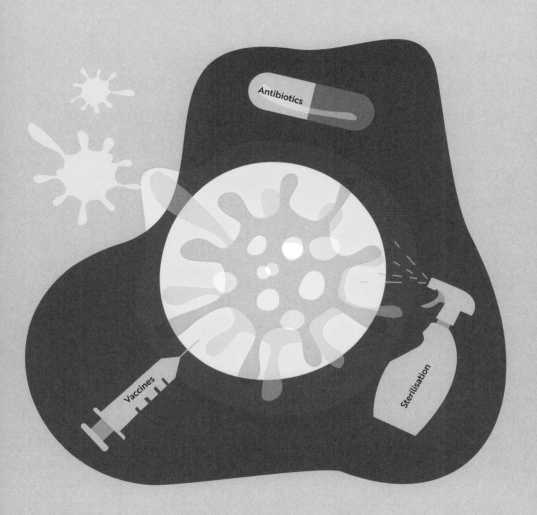

Before germ theory, many people thought that disease was caused by bad air or 'miasma'. Now, it's widely accepted that infectious diseases are caused by 'germs' in the form of bacteria, fungi and other microscopic entities. The war against them is ongoing, with frontline artillery including sterilisation, vaccines and antibiotics. However, as germs evolve, our treatment options must evolve too, so new drugs and vaccines are constantly being developed.

# Are vaccines the only route to immunity?

⟶ **No, they're not. There are different types of immunity and different routes to achieve them. But vaccines, which work by imitating an infection, are an excellent option because they can protect us against diseases we have yet to encounter.**

There are three basic types of immunity. We're all born with some degree of natural or innate immunity, which provides us with a general level of protection against potentially harmful substances, such as germs and toxins. Skin, for example, is part of this system because it acts as a barrier to germs.

Passive immunity, in contrast, is acquired during your lifetime. It is 'borrowed' from another source and only lasts for a short time. Proteins in a mother's breast milk, for example, may give a baby temporary immunity to diseases that the mother has experienced.

Active immunity is also acquired during life, but it is longer lasting. It occurs naturally when we are exposed to a disease-causing organism or 'pathogen', and it involves multiple cell types. Phagocytes, for example, engulf and destroy the pathogens, while lymphocytes help the body to remember previous invaders and recognise them if they come back. They do this by producing antibodies, which recognise proteins on the surface of the pathogens called antigens. This takes time, and during this time we can feel ill.

Vaccines also generate active immunity. They work by fooling the immune system into thinking it is being attacked by a pathogen, so the body can generate immunity without experiencing disease.

Edward Jenner famously invented the smallpox vaccine in 1796. Jenner's vaccine used a live, smallpox-like virus to produce immunity, but today's vaccines tend to be made from dead or altered versions of pathogens. Some, such as the first vaccine to be approved for COVID-19, are made from snippets of genetic code called messenger RNA, which provide the body with the instructions needed to make immune-stimulating proteins.

Collectively, vaccines are one of the biggest public health success stories ever. They have banished smallpox from the world and helped to bring the recent COVID-19 pandemic under control in countries where vaccines are widely available. It's estimated that every year, vaccines prevent around 5 million deaths.

# HOW VACCINES WORK

Pathogen (virus)

Antibodies

Lymphocyte

Vaccines work by tricking the body
into thinking it has been attacked by a
pathogen. They stimulate white blood cells
called lymphocytes to generate antibodies
that latch on to the pathogen and target
it for destruction by other immune cells.
Some vaccines generate immunity that
lasts for decades, while others generate a
shorter-lived immunity that lasts for years
or sometimes only months. This is why, for
example, additional booster shots of the
COVID-19 vaccine are required.

# Is epidemiology bad for our health?

**→ Epidemiology is the study of how often diseases occur in different groups of people and why. It's good for our health because it helps researchers identify the causes of diseases, and the best ways to prevent or control them.**

Florence Nightingale may be well known for her nursing skills, but she was also an accomplished statistician. Working in a dirty, overcrowded Turkish military hospital during the Crimean War (1853–56), she tracked the number of deaths and was able to prove that more soldiers were dying from diseases they picked up on the wards than from battlefield wounds. Then, when hygiene measures were improved, she used data to show that the death rate was dropping. It was the beginning of modern epidemiology, which employs data-driven methods to manage and improve public health.

Around the same time, English physician John Snow was using a similar approach to track a cholera outbreak in Soho, London. By plotting all the cases on a map, he was able to show that the disease emanated from a single water pump in Broad Street. When the pump handle was removed, cases began to fall. This single event further laid the foundations for the science of epidemiology.

Today, epidemiology has broadened its horizons, looking beyond just infectious diseases to all diseases. For example, genome-wide association studies, which compare the DNA of healthy and diseased populations, have identified genetic risk factors that predispose certain people to develop cancer, heart disease and diabetes. Meanwhile, powerful algorithms and intense computing power enable researchers to analyse huge, diverse and often complex data sets, known as big data, placing epidemiology centre stage in our efforts to understand and control the COVID-19 pandemic.

As waves of the coronavirus disease come and go, epidemiological studies help prove the benefits of vaccines, social distancing and other public health measures, while also helping researchers to anticipate the impact of new variants. Alongside this, predictions from studies that model the virus's spread, and analyses of data on infections and deaths, continue to drive policy decisions all over the world.

# THE REPRODUCTION NUMBER

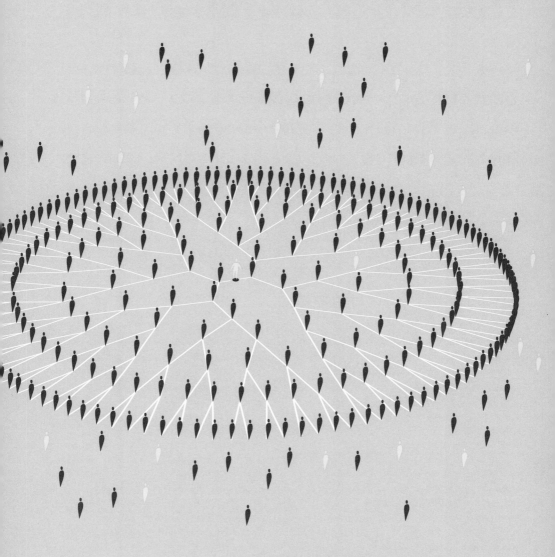

The reproduction number, $R_0$, is a fundamental concept in epidemiology, used to describe the intensity of an infectious disease outbreak. It is the number of cases, on average, that an infected person will cause. If an outbreak has an $R_0$ of two, for example, then each infected person infects two more, who each infect two more, and so on. It shows how a tiny trickle of infections can quickly turn into a deluge.

# What happens when the drugs don't work?

⟶ It's not good news. As more and more bacteria become resistant to the antibiotics we use to kill them, the concern is that once-treatable infections could become deadly.

In 1928, Scottish physician Alexander Fleming left a messy worktop when he went away on holiday – an oversight for which we should all be grateful! When he returned, he spotted that one of the petri dishes he had forgotten to clear away had sprouted mould, and that where the mould grew, bacteria didn't. The mould was oozing a substance that killed bacteria. He initially called it 'mould juice', then later named it penicillin. This, he showed, was effective against all bacteria classified as 'gram-positive', which includes bacteria responsible for diseases such as pneumonia and anthrax.

Penicillin more than proved its worth during the Second World War, when soldiers were at high risk from their infected battle wounds. Penicillin reduced the related mortality rate by around 15 per cent. Since then, antibiotics have paved the way for organ transplants, chemotherapy, caesarean sections and countless other procedures that are now routinely performed with a massively reduced risk of infection. They have saved millions of lives and added twenty years of life expectancy across the globe.

However, in 1945, when Fleming accepted his Nobel Prize for the discovery of penicillin, he predicted the rise of resistance. This wasn't much of a problem before the 1990s, because when an infection became resistant to one antibiotic, there was always another one to use. But that is no longer the case. Some bacteria, such as methicillin-resistant *Staphylococcus aureus* (MRSA), have even become resistant to multiple antibiotics. These are known as superbugs.

A growing number of infections are now becoming harder to treat. The World Health Organization cites antibiotic resistance as one of the biggest threats to global health, food security and development. Scientists estimate that by 2050, it could be responsible for the deaths of 10 million people every year.

So, what's to be done? As researchers race to develop new antibiotics, we need to use the ones that we have sparingly, both in agriculture and in human medicine, to slow down the rise of resistance.

# THE RISE OF RESISTANCE

Imagine an enormous pool of cyclists, some with helmets, some without. When collisions occur, the ones without helmets are more likely to die, so over time the riders with helmets predominate. Similarly, bacteria that are resistant to antibiotics have a survival advantage over bacteria that are killed by these life-saving medicines; again, over time, antibiotic-resistant bacteria come to predominate. Antibacterial resistance is now a major concern that threatens to derail decades of progress in public health.

# How do we reprogramme a cell?

⟶ Cellular reprogramming is a bit like restoring the factory settings on your phone. Getting adult cells to transition into a more youthful state holds great promise for regenerative medicine, fertility treatments and drug design.

Cellular reprogramming is the ability of scientists to turn mature, specialised adult cells, such as skin cells, into versatile, intermediate cells called stem cells, which can then be coaxed to become any cell of choice.

For someone with Parkinson's disease or kidney failure, for example, a skin sample could be used to generate new neural or renal tissue, which could then be used to repair the damaged organ. A woman with fertility problems could have the technique used to generate eggs for in vitro fertilisation (IVF). Or, because the cells are perfectly matched to the patient, the technique could be used to determine which treatments are best suited to them. That all sounds great, but how does it work?

In the early days, cellular reprogramming was achieved through cloning. In 1962, British scientist John Gurdon showed that specialised cells from a tadpole's intestine could be reprogrammed when their DNA was transferred into an empty egg cell. The reconfigured cell began to divide, and then developed into a tadpole that was a clone of the original amphibian.

Scientists who performed similar experiments with mammalian cells realised that these early cloned embryos could be used as a source of stem cells for regenerative medicine. But they faced an ethical dilemma: when the stem cells were harvested, the embryo was destroyed.

The problem was solved in 2006 when Japanese biologist and Nobel prize winner Shinya Yamanaka came up with an embryo-free way of making stem cells. His solution was to add four key genes to cultured mouse skin cells. He called these cells 'induced pluripotent stem cells' or iPSCs, and they've since been used to generate many cell types, including liver, blood, brain and beating heart cells. The method continues to be improved, and clinical trials are in their infancy, but cellular reprogramming holds great promise for the future of modern medicine.

# THE PROMISE OF REGENERATIVE MEDICINE

*Cellular reprogramming can be used to generate cells for organ repair and drug screening.*

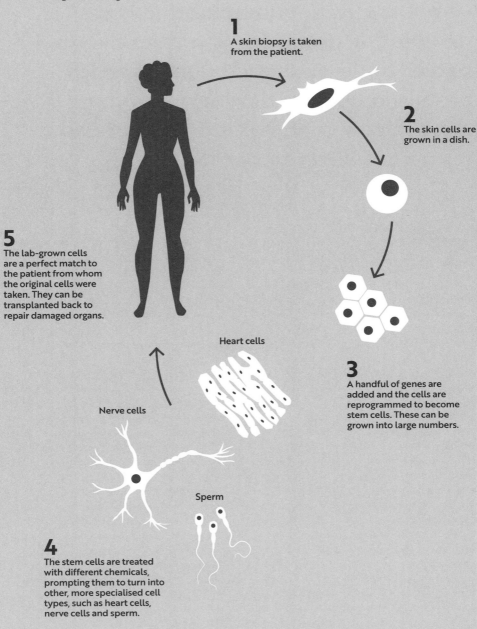

**1** A skin biopsy is taken from the patient.

**2** The skin cells are grown in a dish.

**3** A handful of genes are added and the cells are reprogrammed to become stem cells. These can be grown into large numbers.

**4** The stem cells are treated with different chemicals, prompting them to turn into other, more specialised cell types, such as heart cells, nerve cells and sperm.

**5** The lab-grown cells are a perfect match to the patient from whom the original cells were taken. They can be transplanted back to repair damaged organs.

Heart cells

Nerve cells

Sperm

# Is gene editing good news or bad news?

**→ From gene-edited food to cures for devastating disorders, and from designer babies to de-extinction, the advances promised by gene editing are nothing if not controversial. But is it good or bad? It's up to society to decide.**

In 2012, biologists Jennifer Doudna and Emmanuelle Charpentier demonstrated how a simple molecular system, called CRISPR-Cas9, could be used to precisely cut DNA. Genes had been altered or 'edited' before, but never with this level of accuracy.

CRISPR-Cas9 is cheaper, easier and more versatile than previous methods, and it enables researchers to add, remove or alter specific DNA sequences at will, effectively rewriting the code of life.

In the space of just one decade, researchers have since used CRISPR-Cas9 to make disease-resistant chickens, heat-tolerant cattle and woollier sheep. They've made drought-resistant maize, higher-yield rice and potatoes with a longer shelf life. In conservation, it's being touted as a way to control the reproduction of problematic invasive species and to bring back or 'de-extinct' extinct species, such as the woolly mammoth.

Meanwhile, in medicine, the technique is being used to switch off genes inside cells, one at a time, to see what they do, and to create better models of disease. It's already been used as a therapy in a small number of patients, where it has improved symptoms in people with certain genetic disorders, such as sickle cell disease, and it's currently being developed as a treatment for more common diseases, such as cancer.

The most controversial application, however, involves using CRISPR-Cas9 to permanently alter the DNA of future descendants. In 2018, Chinese scientist He Jiankui announced the birth of the world's first CRISPR babies: twin girls engineered to be resistant to human immunodeficiency virus (HIV). His decision to alter the human germline, meaning the edits he made will be passed down the generations, was a move that sparked widespread condemnation as many felt he had crossed an ethical line. Critics pointed out that the long-term repercussions of such edits are unknown and, in 2020, an international panel of scientific societies concluded that the technique is not ready for use on human embryos. How will things change in the future? Only time will tell.

# REWRITING THE CODE OF LIFE

CRISPR-Cas9 is a technique that enables scientists to precisely rewrite the code of life – DNA. It's been likened to a pair of molecular scissors being guided by a tiny satnav. Genes can be altered, removed or added, and DNA from one species can even be added into the genome of another.

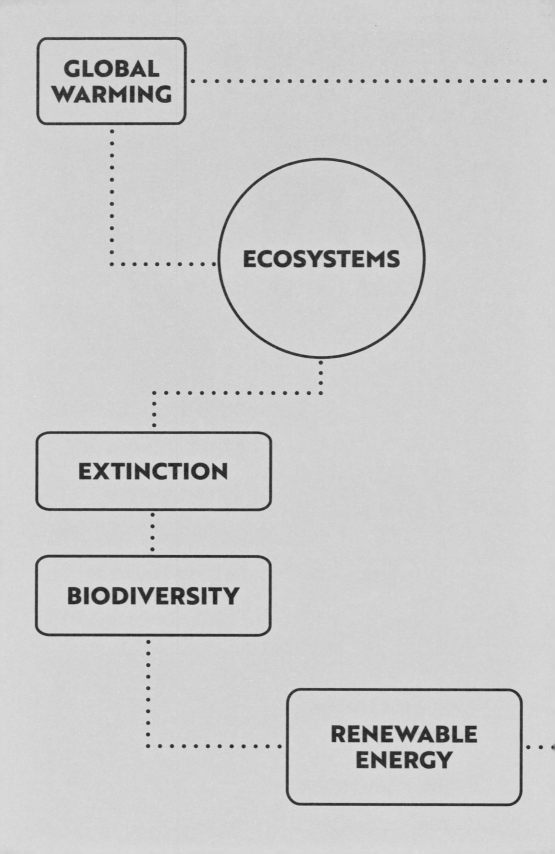

# CHAPTER 7

# WORLDS

EXOPLANET

DRAKE EQUATION

EXTRATERRESTRIAL LIFE

# INTRODUCTION

As biologists drill ever deeper into the molecular mysteries of life, other scientists are zooming outwards to take a more holistic view of the Earth and its inhabitants. Studying life at the planetary scale can show how species interact within an ecosphere – and how a single species can sometimes have world-altering effects.

Take **GLOBAL WARMING**, which is being driven by human-made emissions of carbon dioxide, methane and other **GREENHOUSE GASES** (see page 124). Unless we limit these emissions, **CLIMATE CHANGE** will trigger a growing number of extreme weather events such as heatwaves and floods, potentially displacing millions of people and putting **ECOSYSTEMS** under enormous strain. If you want a glimpse of what extreme climate change can do, look no further than the Permian-Triassic **EXTINCTION**, a natural global-warming event that took place 252 million years ago and wiped out about 90 per cent of all species.

Species typically depend on each other for survival – predators need prey, insects pollinate flowers, and so on. This essential variety of life is called **BIODIVERSITY** and it is in shocking decline (see page 126). Scientists estimate that about 1 million species could become extinct in the next few decades.

A great deal of biodiversity loss is caused by human activity such as logging, farming and fishing. Increasingly, people are recognising that profligate consumption of the Earth's resources is unsustainable, and many argue that there are natural limits to the growth of a global economy that is based on exploiting finite resources (see page 128). This is now spurring efforts to move away from our throwaway lifestyles and instead pursue a **CIRCULAR ECONOMY** that conserves our planet's precious resources. **RENEWABLE ENERGY**, for example, could play a huge role in making that transition (see page 130).

The Earth is a very special place, but it is probably just one of trillions of planets peppered through our galaxy. For centuries, astronomers only knew the handful of planets that orbit our own Sun. But in 1992 they detected the first **EXOPLANET** – a world that circles around a distant star – and since then they have spotted more than 5,000 different exoplanets (see page 132).

Could any of them host intelligent life? If aliens do live on other planets, we haven't heard from them yet. But scientists involved in the search for extraterrestrial intelligence (**SETI**) are listening hard for alien transmissions. One way to rate their chances is the **DRAKE EQUATION**, a formula for estimating how many technologically advanced societies exist on habitable planets throughout the galaxy (see page 134). There's no agreed answer; currently, estimates vary from one (yes, that's us) to millions. But the equation has certainly helped guide astronomers to the sorts of places they should be looking for extraterrestrial life.

It's possible that an exoplanet society is already well aware of human civilisation. But perhaps they have seen the impact we are having on our own planet and have decided to stay quiet for now.

# WORLDS MAP

## POLLUTION

### GREENHOUSE GAS
Gas emitted by natural or human activity that traps heat in the Earth's atmosphere: includes carbon dioxide and methane.

### FOSSIL FUELS
Naturally occurring materials containing hydrogen and carbon made from buried decomposing plants and animals that can be burned to produce energy: includes coal, oil and natural gas.

### RENEWABLE ENERGY
Energy generated from sources that are not finite, such as solar energy from the Sun, wind power and hydroelectric power from moving water.

### GLOBAL WARMING
Increase in temperatures on Earth caused by greenhouse gases in the atmosphere; usually referring to heating of the climate system since the pre-industrial period.

### CLIMATE CHANGE
Long-term shifts in Earth's temperature and weather patterns due to global warming; predicted to include sea-level rise and increased frequency and severity of storms, flooding and droughts.

### ENVIRONMENT
The surroundings or conditions that an organism lives in; or the combination of all living and non-living constituents of our Earth, including air, water, plants and animals.

### LIMITS TO GROWTH
A 1972 study showing that endless economic expansion is environmentally unsustainable.

### CIRCULAR ECONOMY
Closed-loop approach to production and consumption designed to avoid waste by reusing, repairing, refurbishing, recycling, and also sharing and leasing.

### EXOPLANET
Any planet outside our solar system.

# ECOLOGY

**TIPPING POINT**
Any threshold in a system beyond which it is impossible to reverse its state or stop a change happening.

**EXTINCTION**
When every individual of a species has died.

**ECOSYSTEM**
Group of organisms and their physical environment that interact with each other in a geographical 'bubble'.

**BIODIVERSITY**
The variety of all life on Earth, including animals, plants, fungi and micro-organisms such as bacteria and amoeba.

**FOOD CHAIN**
Linked series of organisms that each depend on another as a source of food, starting with one that makes its own food, such as a plant.

**INVASIVE SPECIES**
Non-native species that harms a new environment to which it has been introduced by humans (on purpose or accidentally), usually due to overpopulation.

# ALIENS

**GOLDILOCKS ZONE**
Region of space around a star where conditions mean water on an exoplanet could remain liquid and therefore might support forms of life.

**SETI**
Search for extraterrestrial intelligence – the hunt for intelligent life on other planets in our galaxy, typically by analysing electromagnetic signals from space.

**DRAKE EQUATION**
Method devised by astronomer Frank Drake for determining how many exoplanets in the Milky Way galaxy might host technologically advanced civilisations.

# Can global warming destroy a planet?

**⟶ If, by 'destroy', we mean can it render all life on a planet extinct, then yes. We have evidence from the fossil record that mass extinctions have happened in Earth's past, but this time there's a different culprit.**

The Permian-Triassic extinction 252 million years ago eradicated about 90 per cent of Earth's species. It was almost certainly caused by a surge in global warming and the resulting increase in atmospheric carbon dioxide ($CO_2$) released from volcanic eruptions in present-day Siberia. $CO_2$ is one of numerous gases that create a greenhouse effect, forming an atmospheric barrier that prevents heat loss.

Of course, this was a natural event that took place across millions of years. The bad news is the rate of global warming today is almost ten times faster and is caused by human activity, such as burning fossil fuels and deforestation. This produces more $CO_2$ and other greenhouse gases such as nitrous oxide. If this continues at this pace, extreme weather events – storms, heatwaves, floods – will only worsen. Polar ice caps and glaciers will melt further, as will permafrost (releasing more carbon). Sea levels will rise and desertification will increase, meaning mass extinction is only decades away, if it hasn't already begun.

Ultimately, starvation following the destruction of the food chain will cause the extermination of life. When a food chain's base – such as insects, krill or plankton – dies as the environment changes, bigger animals that feed on smaller animals also perish. Climate scientists predict this could begin with warming of only 1.5°C above pre-industrial levels, which is likely to happen by 2050. Currently, the world has already warmed by 1.2°C.

Once the tipping point – when small changes cause profound, irreversible shifts – is reached, runaway climate change will be unstoppable. This point may be as little as 2°C above pre-industrialised levels.

The end of life will be characterised by collapsing ecosystems, rampant pollution, scarce fresh water, forest death and the destruction of farmland from migrating pests or drought. The seas will heat, lack oxygen and acidify. New or once dormant diseases will emerge. Heatstroke will be commonplace and human migration necessary and constant, leading to conflict and economic collapse.

Evolutionary studies indicate most species won't adapt rapidly enough to counter such environmental changes. Whether humanity will act in time hangs in the balance.

# COLLAPSING ECOSYSTEM

The rise in atmospheric $CO_2$ was first noticed 120 years ago; then decades later, chemist Charles Keeling confirmed human activity was causing the ever-increasing levels of this potent greenhouse gas. In 1988, the Intergovernmental Panel on Climate Change was founded to coordinate research into the issue. But since then, humanity as a whole has paid little heed to the warning signs of our planet overheating – either missing internationally agreed targets for reduction of greenhouse gas emissions or choosing to ignore the subject altogether.

Sea levels may rise by 75 cm this century.

Thermal expansion of water contributes 42 per cent to sea level rise.

The warmest seven years in history have all been since 2015.

# How diverse is our biodiversity?

⟶ **Not as diverse as it should be. Life on Earth needs a diverse range of organisms to help form and support the ecosystems that provide life-sustaining services, such as fresh water, food and medicines.**

Biodiversity is the variety of all life on Earth, including animals, plants, fungi and micro-organisms such as bacteria and amoeba. It jostles along, as well as it can, interacting with the physical environment around it, to form ecosystems. Mangrove swamps, for example, help to prevent erosion and act as a buffer against storm damage. Tropical rainforests provide homes for millions of species, sequester carbon inside the trees that grow there, and release oxygen into the air for all of us to breathe. These benefits, however, do not come from a single species. They come from different species interacting. In other words, we need biodiversity.

Although there is a normal background extinction rate, rates of extinction are currently spiking. Species are disappearing between 1,000 and 10,000 times more quickly than scientists would normally expect. It's estimated that around 1 million species could go extinct in the next few decades, including 40 per cent of amphibians, 33 per cent of reef-dwelling corals, 34 per cent of conifers, 31 per cent of sharks and rays, 25 per cent of mammals and 14 per cent of birds. Biodiversity is in decline.

Scientists dispute the possible repercussions. Some argue that when ecosystems pass a tipping point, they will collapse. Others argue that Earth has been through mass extinctions like this before and that life will bounce back. But this could take tens of thousands of years. So, what's to be done?

The problem is one of our own making. Climate change is making it difficult for many plants and animals to survive. Logging, hunting and fishing are decimating wild species, as are intensive agricultural practices and the spread of troublesome invasive species. International groups are working together to try to reverse this decline. At the same time, individuals can play their part by setting land aside for nature, eating more plants and consuming less and better meat from pasture-fed, free-range and organic systems.

# THE PERILS OF BIODIVERSITY LOSS

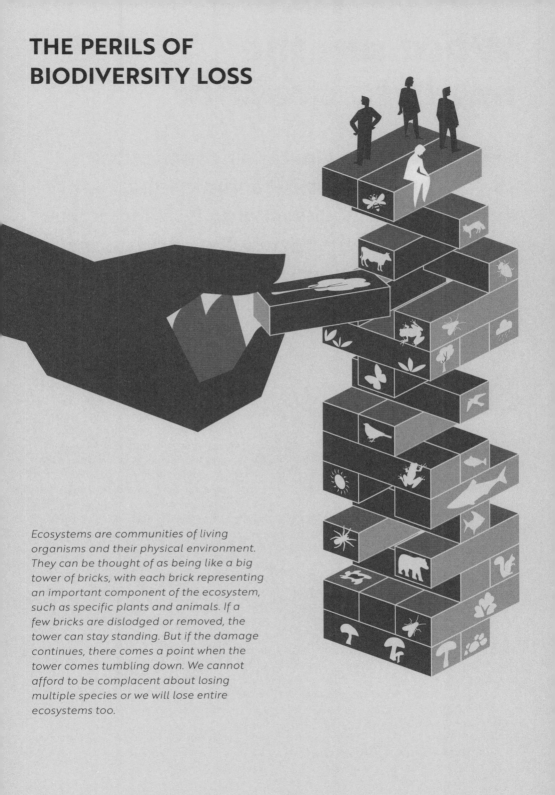

Ecosystems are communities of living organisms and their physical environment. They can be thought of as being like a big tower of bricks, with each brick representing an important component of the ecosystem, such as specific plants and animals. If a few bricks are dislodged or removed, the tower can stay standing. But if the damage continues, there comes a point when the tower comes tumbling down. We cannot afford to be complacent about losing multiple species or we will lose entire ecosystems too.

# What are the limits to growth?

**⟶ In 1972, *The Limits to Growth* study showed that endless economic expansion is environmentally unsustainable. Then, it was hugely controversial; now the conclusions seem obvious, supporting environmentalism and the concept of a 'circular economy'.**

Back in the early 1970s, a growing number of scientists were waking up to the probable environmental consequences of a turbocharged global economy. These concerns were crystallised in a hugely influential report called *The Limits To Growth*, which had been commissioned by The Club of Rome, a global forum for politicians, scientists, economists and business leaders.

*The Limits to Growth* set out to study how factors such as population growth, consumption of natural resources and pollution would shape our world in the future. It marked an early milestone in the use of computer simulations to extrapolate how key variables affect global outcomes.

The results mostly painted a bleak picture. If society continued on its current trajectory, the report said, our upward spiral of consumption would overshoot the Earth's capacity to support it within a century. The outcome would be a sudden, massive collapse in human civilisation. In other words, economies cannot keep growing indefinitely on a finite planet.

Many commentators at the time decried the report as fear-mongering nonsense. Critics said the report's underlying data was flawed, the computer simulations were too simplistic and even that the authors were motivated by a sinister, anti-capitalist agenda.

And yet as time went on, *The Limits to Growth* began to look remarkably prescient as the damage humans were causing to the environment became increasingly apparent. The report, published as a book, became an influential bestseller and a lodestone for the growing environmental movement. More recently, sophisticated computer models have repeated the analyses in the report, and generally support its conclusions.

Fifty years on, there is ample evidence that we are pushing the Earth's life-support systems to breaking point. Pollution, resource depletion and climate change have all become enormous issues that command global attention.

Alongside the doom and gloom, though, *The Limits to Growth* also contained some hopeful conclusions. By reigning in consumption, it said, we should be able to alter our greedy trajectory of growth and reach a state of economic and ecological stability. The choice is ours.

# A CIRCULAR ECONOMY

Our economy is described as 'linear'; natural resources are used to manufacture products that eventually become waste, in an endless conveyor belt that depletes Earth's capacity to sustain human life. The Limits to Growth study spurred researchers to seek alternative economic models, including the so-called circular economy.

In this model, products that have reached the end of their useful life are either reused, refurbished or recycled, in processes driven by renewable energy (see page 130). This not only minimises waste, but also reduces the amount of raw materials needed to produce new goods.

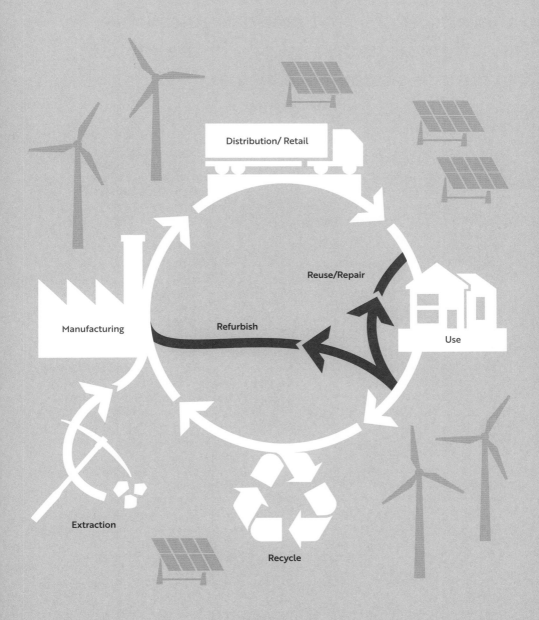

Distribution/ Retail

Reuse/Repair

Manufacturing

Refurbish

Use

Extraction

Recycle

# How can we renew Earth's energy?

**⟶ Hydroelectricity, wind, solar, biofuels, geothermal and tidal are all renewable power sources that could help to wean us off fossil fuels, and power the planet in a more sustainable way.**

The modern world is largely powered by fossil fuels such as coal, oil and gas. Oil is refined to make fuel, such as petrol and jet fuel, for transport. Gas boilers warm our homes. And power stations burn these hydrocarbons to generate electricity.

The problem is that freeing the energy locked up in fossil fuels typically produces large amounts of carbon dioxide ($CO_2$) – a greenhouse gas that spells bad news for the climate (see page 124).

That's one of the main reasons why the world is racing to get its energy from renewable energy sources instead, from the Sun, wind, and crops that can be turned into fuels. Solar and wind power never run out. And crucially, none of them directly emit $CO_2$. Fossil fuels often emit other air pollutants when they burn, so renewables can also help us breathe more easily.

Renewable power is making real progress. In 2020, renewables supplied more than 28 per cent of the world's electricity. Most of this comes from solar panels, wind turbines and hydroelectric power facilities.

Building solar panels was once expensive. But mass manufacturing and some improvements in the underlying technology, mean that costs have plummeted. Between 2010 and 2020, the cost of electricity generated by solar panels fell by an average of 82 per cent; in sunny spots, the panels now produce cheaper electricity than coal-fired power stations.

Here's how they work. Most solar cells contain a semiconductor called silicon. When light hits this material, it excites an electron in silicon's crystalline structure, leaving behind a positively-charged 'hole'. The electrons travel to one electrode, while the holes go to the opposite electrode. Collectively, this flow of charge generates an electrical current.

Unfortunately, solar and wind power are not much use on a windless night. That's why we also need different ways to store renewable energy, using large batteries or hydroelectric reservoirs.

Despite renewable electricity capacity growing by roughly 7 per cent per year, this still only meets about half of the expected increase in global energy demand. Renewables are beneficial, but they are no panacea – we also need to curb our growing energy use (see page 128).

# GLOBAL ENERGY USE

Renewables can supply clean electricity that should help us to shut down polluting fossil fuel power stations. But it's important to remember that electricity only accounts for about 22 per cent of the world's overall energy use today. So while renewables are being rolled out, we also need to electrify more of the transport, heavy industry and other energy-intensive sectors that currently depend on burning fossil fuels directly, so that they too can benefit from the renewables revolution.

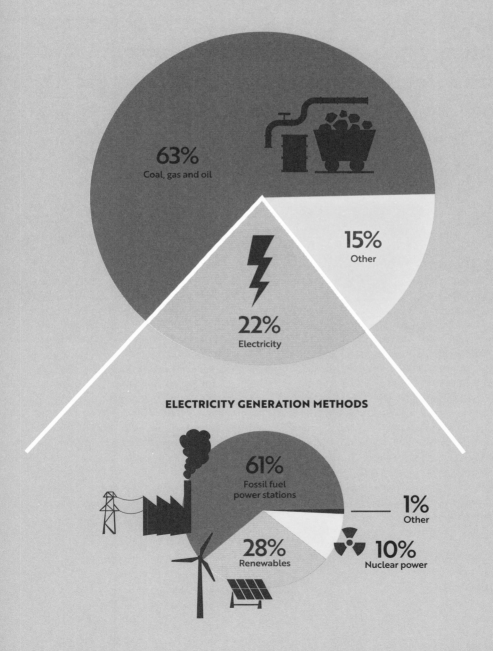

**63%**
Coal, gas and oil

**15%**
Other

**22%**
Electricity

## ELECTRICITY GENERATION METHODS

**61%**
Fossil fuel power stations

**1%**
Other

**28%**
Renewables

**10%**
Nuclear power

# Could Goldilocks lead us to aliens?

→ **Possibly. Some exoplanets sit in the 'Goldilocks zone', not so close to a star that all water evaporates and not so far away that all water freezes (think about Goldilocks eating porridge). And where there's liquid water, there might be alien life.**

Our solar system contains eight planets, from small scorched Mercury to the ice giant Neptune. But beyond our cosmic backyard, there are hundreds of billions of stars in the Milky Way, and perhaps 2 trillion galaxies in the universe. That's an awful lot of stars, and many of them are circled by far-flung worlds called exoplanets.

Italian philosopher Giordano Bruno speculated in the 16th century that stars could have their own planetary systems, but it wasn't until 1992 that astronomers confirmed the existence of an exoplanet for the first time. Since then, they have come thick and fast: the exoplanet tally now tops 5,000. Astronomers have found some exoplanets by measuring how they make their stars wobble as they orbit. Other exoplanets show themselves by slightly dimming the light from their star as they pass across its face. Powerful telescopes have even been able to see a few exoplanets directly. Most of the early exoplanet discoveries were 'hot Jupiters', gas-giant planets orbiting close to their stars. But as exoplanet hunters improved their techniques and used better kit such as the Kepler space telescope, they started to find more rocky, Earth-like planets.

NASA's James Webb Space Telescope has opened a new window on these worlds. It studies infrared light shining through the atmospheres of exoplanets, looking for molecules that could form the building blocks of life (see page 22). It is also revealing more about how planets are born from the primordial disks of dust and gas around young stars.

By looking deep into space, we may yet learn more about the origins of our planet, or even discover that we are not alone ...

# THE GOLDILOCKS ZONE

← Too cold    **Just right**    Too hot →

In the classic children's fairy tale, Goldilocks chooses Little Bear's bowl of porridge because it is not too hot and not too cold: instead, it is 'just right'. She now lends her name to the Goldilocks zone – the area of space around a star where an orbiting exoplanet is at just the right distance to have a temperature such that liquid water, and therefore life, might be able to exist.

# Is there anybody out there?

**⟶ If there is, they're keeping quiet. But the universe is so vast that many scientists believe there must be intelligent life on other planets. The Drake Equation offers one way to estimate whether we might one day hear from them.**

NASA scientists think there could be up to 300 million habitable exoplanets in our galaxy, the Milky Way. But how many of them might host alien civilisations capable of communication? In 1961, astronomer Frank Drake came up with a method for making a good guess.

The Drake Equation includes seven factors, such as how often life might appear on a habitable planet and the chances of it evolving into a technologically advanced society. Although the equation has no solution, some estimates suggest that there could be thousands of such civilisations across our galaxy.

Despite its inherent uncertainties, the Drake Equation also gave scientists a road map for exploring questions around the existence of alien life, which galvanised the search for extraterrestrial intelligence (SETI).

SETI researchers typically use radio telescopes to listen for alien transmissions, but they haven't detected any convincing signals yet. So if the universe is supposedly teeming with habitable worlds, why have we not heard from aliens? This is known as the Fermi Paradox, named after physicist Enrico Fermi who pointed out the anomaly. Perhaps it means that intelligent life is far rarer than we think, or that civilisations often burn out before they can develop interstellar communication.

Closer to home, various space probes have carried equipment that could find chemical traces of simpler lifeforms on other worlds. In 1976, a pair of Viking spacecraft landed on Mars and ran experiments looking for signs of life, but the results were ambiguous at best. Several other Mars missions since then have found hints of biological activity on Mars – whiffs of methane, for example – but that could be explained by geology, rather than biology. In the coming decade, planned space probes will hunt for signs of life on Europa and Titan, moons that orbit Jupiter and Saturn, respectively.

Doing this kind of chemical analysis on other planets is hard. NASA's Perseverance rover is collecting Martian rock samples that will be returned to Earth in the 2030s, potentially giving scientists the best chance yet of finding signs of alien life.

# INTERSTELLAR MESSAGE
# IN A BOTTLE

Radio waves aren't the only way of sending
messages into space. In the early 1970s,
the Pioneer 10 and 11 space probes carried
plaques engraved with a map showing the
location of our solar system, and Earth's
place within it, along with an illustration of a
naked man and woman. In 1977, two Voyager
probes each carried a gold disc that
contained recordings of music, greetings
and other sounds from Earth – along with
instructions telling alien DJs how to play it.
The Voyager craft have now left our solar
system, carrying their messages
into interstellar space.

TECHNOLOGICAL
REVOLUTION

SCIENTIFIC
METHOD

INTERNATIONAL
SYSTEM OF UNITS

INFORMATION
THEORY

# CHAPTER 8

# INFORMATION

QUANTUM COMPUTERS

CHAOS THEORY

GAME THEORY

MACHINE LEARNING

# INTRODUCTION

**A**s we've learned, science is brilliant at figuring out how things work. But how does science itself work?

Science often starts with an observation that cannot be explained. Scientists then come up with a hypothesis about how this strange event might have occurred and devise an experiment to test their idea. This combination of observation, hypothesis and experiment really caught on during the **SCIENTIFIC REVOLUTION** of the 16th and 17th centuries and laid the foundations for the way that professional science happens today (see page 142).

Despite what you might have heard, there isn't a single **SCIENTIFIC METHOD** – but somewhere along the line you can bet that science will involve some very careful measurements. Scientists are always trying to reproduce each other's experiments, so they need an agreed system of measurements to make sure their results are comparable. That framework is called the **INTERNATIONAL SYSTEM OF UNITS** (see page 144). This used to depend on physical objects to define standard quantities, but scientists now define these measurements by the fundamental constants of nature, such as the speed of light in a vacuum.

Information is an essential ingredient for science, but it increasingly dominates our everyday lives too. The enormous quantities of data that whizz around the globe are largely transmitted in digital form, with messages encoded in a staccato series of 1s and 0s known as bits. **INFORMATION THEORY** helps engineers to work out new ways to cram ever more data through communication channels, or how to store that information in chips and on magnetic disks (see page 146).

Information theory offers one approach to studying incredibly complex systems. Another is **CHAOS THEORY**, based on the idea that making tiny changes to a complex system – such as the Earth's weather patterns – can have dramatic and unexpected outcomes (see page 148). A third view of complexity emerges from **GAME THEORY**, which describes how conflict, cooperation and decision making happen in areas as diverse as evolution and economics (see page 150).

We can also use information to train computers, honing their skills so that they become better at playing chess or spotting problems in medical scans. This is called **MACHINE LEARNING**, and it involves pouring sample data into a computer until it starts to spot recurring connections between actions and outcomes (see page 152). The computer gains so much experience of cause and effect that it effectively 'learns' how to predict those connections in the future.

**QUANTUM COMPUTERS** could turbocharge machine learning and many other areas of computing (see page 154). Whereas classical computers rely on binary bits, a quantum computer processes information that is stored in the quantum states of subatomic particles. These 'qubits' can represent both a 1 and a 0 at the same time, which in principle gives quantum computers the ability to simultaneously calculate all of the possible solutions to some fiendishly difficult problems. It's early days, but the weirdness of the quantum world could eventually give us computers that usher in a new era of accelerated scientific discovery.

# INFORMATION MAP

## SCIENCE

### SCIENTIFIC METHOD

The process scientists use to explain an aspect of the natural world, consisting of: question, hypothesis, prediction, experiment, analysis, conclusion.

### SCIENTIFIC REVOLUTION

Period of significant discoveries and change in attitudes towards science and the natural world during the 16th and 17th centuries, marking the emergence of modern science.

### THEORY

In science, a formal, structured explanation of an aspect of the natural world taking into account any existing laws and known facts.

### GAME THEORY

Mathematics of strategies associated with competitive situations, used to model the outcomes of conflict versus cooperation.

### CHAOS THEORY

Explains how minor differences in the initial conditions of a complex dynamic system can yield divergent, seemingly random, outcomes; links small-scale order and patterns to apparent chaos at a large scale.

### JOHN VON NEUMANN

Hungarian-American mathematician (1903–57) who pioneered modern game theory and coined the term 'zero-sum' for two-person games where one person's loss is another's gain.

### BUTTERFLY EFFECT

Refers to chaos theory, after Edward Lorenz described it in a 1972 talk entitled 'Does the flap of a butterfly's wings in Brazil set off a tornado in Texas?'

**DATA**

**EXPERIMENT**
Test or procedure to test a hypothesis or theory, demonstrate a fact or make a discovery.

**PHYSICAL CONSTANTS**
Values that are universal and known to never vary, such as the speed of light in a vacuum or the electrical charge of a single electron; used to define the base SI units.

**UNIT (OF MEASUREMENT)**
Standard defined quantity used to describe how much of something there is, usually adopted by convention or law for consistency.

**INTERNATIONAL SYSTEM OF UNITS (SI)**
Global common standard for units of measurement, with seven base units: mass (kilogram), length (metre), time (second), electric current (ampere), temperature (kelvin), amount of substance (mole) and luminous intensity (candela).

**INFORMATION THEORY**
Study of the conditions and parameters that govern the transmission and storage of information in communication systems.

**NEURAL NETWORKS**
Subset of machine learning intended to simulate the way human brains operate by using algorithms to recognise underlying patterns in data sets without having to follow comprehensive lists of instructions.

**TURING TEST**
Originally called the Imitation Game by mathematician and computer scientist Alan Turing, a three-person test to determine whether a machine can demonstrate intelligence equivalent to a human.

**BIT**
Binary digit – most basic unit of information in computing and digital communications, with a value of 0 or 1.

**MACHINE LEARNING**
Subset of AI; a computer system that analyses large amounts of labelled data for patterns and links, using these to learn and adapt how it performs a task.

**ARTIFICIAL INTELLIGENCE (AI)**
Intelligence demonstrated by machines, especially computers, enabling them to independently undertake tasks usually performed by humans.

**QUANTUM COMPUTER**
Device that uses the quantum states of subatomic particles to process information. Quantum supremacy is when a quantum computer solves a problem no classical computer can solve in any reasonable amount of time.

**QUBIT**
Quantum bit – basic unit of information in a quantum computer.

# What is critical to the scientific method?

→ **Question, hypothesis, prediction, experiment, analysis and conclusion are the key steps of the scientific method. People may disagree about exactly how science works, but modern science wouldn't exist without these investigative processes.**

How do we acquire knowledge about the world around us? By doing science, of course. But it has not always been obvious *how* to do science.

People did scientific work long before it was called science. Thousands of years ago, astronomers made detailed observations of the stars and planets, while metallurgists experimented with ores of copper and tin to perfect their recipe for bronze.

Yet much of natural philosophy, as it was once known, relied more on deep thought than measurements and experiments. Many natural philosophers thought they could use pure logic to find truths about the world, using reasoning by deduction. However, some pointed out that they could gather scientific knowledge from direct experience. One early proponent of this idea was Ibn al-Haytham, a great experimental scientist who studied light, lenses and other aspects of optics in Egypt in the early 11th century.

This approach flourished during a period of incredible advances known as the Scientific Revolution. One of its stars, English philosopher Francis Bacon, set down a protocol in the 17th century for doing science by making observations and recording facts, and using them to formulate theories. Meanwhile, French philosopher and mathematician René Descartes promoted the idea that scientists could explain the world through measurements and mathematics.

Scientists increasingly used experiments to test their theories. Many scientists now believe that a theory is only truly scientific if it is falsifiable – in other words, you should be able to do an experiment that proves the theory is false.

Experiments also need to be reproducible, so that other scientists can repeat them to check the results. It can take decades of work, involving many different scientists, before a theory becomes broadly accepted as 'true' – or as close to the truth as we're able to get.

Above all, the scientific method depends on testing ideas with experimental evidence, rather than simply accepting what a professor says. The motto of the Royal Society, the UK's fellowship organisation for eminent global scientists, is: *Nullius in verba*. Roughly translated, it means 'Take nobody's word for it'. That's a pretty good maxim for life, not just science.

# THE ROUTE OF KNOWLEDGE

*Here's one way to map out the scientific method. First, scientists see something they don't understand. They come up with a hypothesis to explain what they've seen. Then they use the hypothesis to make a prediction and carry out an experiment to gather evidence that will confirm or refute that prediction. In fact, there is no single scientific method, and philosophers of science still argue about how science works. But for aspiring Einsteins, this simple model is not a bad place to start.*

# How constant is the International System of Units?

→ **Very constant indeed, these days. Scientists once used objects to serve as the standards for measurement. Now, these units are defined by seven fundamental constants that give scientists worldwide an international language of measurement.**

Units of measurement used to be somewhat ambiguous. A cubit was based on the distance from the elbow to the tip of the middle finger, for example, but a Mesopotamian cubit didn't match an Egyptian cubit. Even worse, odd units proliferated – does anyone remember how many perches make a rood?

That was troublesome for scientists, who like nothing more than a really, really precise measurement.

From the 1790s, the French Academy of Sciences, infused with revolutionary zeal, developed the metric system to provide a more logical set of units. Still, there was some inconsistency in how the metric system was applied and how its base units were defined. So in the 1880s, scientists agreed on a global standard for the metre and the kilogram. More followed, and in 1960 these were all brought together into the International System of Units, generally known as the SI.

The SI has seven core units of measurement, including the second, the metre and the kilogram. Some of these were once defined by pristine objects. For example, a cylinder of platinum-iridium alloy served as the one true kilogram for more than a century. Known as Le Grand K, it was kept in an underground vault in Sèvres, France.

Many other copies of this kilogram were made and sent around the world to serve as standard kilograms in each nation, helping to calibrate weighing scales. Over the decades, some of these offspring kilograms changed mass by a few dozen micrograms by absorbing gases from the air. But Le Grande K remained a sacrosanct 1 kilogram – not because its mass hadn't changed, but because it was, by definition, *the* kilogram.

Since 2019, though, all seven of the core units have instead been defined by immutable physical constants, such as the speed of light in a vacuum, or the electrical charge of a single electron. The kilogram is now calculated from Planck's constant. This incredibly small number is the energy of any photon of light divided by its frequency, a number that should be the same everywhere in the known universe. Take that, cubits.

# THE MEASURE OF THINGS

Second, metre, kilogram, ampere, kelvin, mole and candela: these are the base units that allow scientists to measure everything in the universe. Almost two dozen other official SI units are derived from these magnificent seven, including becquerels to measure radioactivity and henrys to measure electrical inductance. Although some of these units were once defined by physical objects, they are now all based on fundamental constants, such as Planck's constant (h).

**Plank's constant is used to define the kilogram.**

**Old measurements included feet, hands and knots.**

# How did information theory start a revolution?

**⟶ By breaking down how we transmit information into its simplest form. It has led to some of technology's most significant advancements, from artificial intelligence and telecommunications to the internet.**

The foundations of information theory were laid out by American electrical engineer Claude Shannon in his 1948 paper *A Mathematical Theory of Communication,* later expanded into a book co-written with Warren Weaver. Shannon was interested in discovering the maximum amount of information that a given communication channel – such as a copper wire or a radio – could transmit. Specifically, he wanted to find new ways to make the transfer of information more efficient and to ascertain how fast coded digital information could be transmitted and processed.

Before information theory, remote communication was carried by analogue signals; for example, a message transmitted along a wire. Shannon knew the signal would degrade the further it had to travel and suffer from fluctuations known as noise.

But he realised that if you could break down the units of information into small blocks that could not be divided any further – units that he called binary digits, or bits –

these could be used to improve the quality of communications. Messages converted into strings of bits, most commonly represented as 1s and 0s, could be transmitted down the wire and rebuilt by the receiver. Even after allowing for signal deterioration and noise, they can still be picked up and reconstructed because they are so simply defined.

Information theory showed how codes could be made more efficient and increase the speed that computers could process information. It has been crucial to the development of mobile phones and formats such as CDs and DVDs. It has provided the mathematical basis for increased data storage and constant increases in the ability of the internet and other media to provide rapid, high-definition information. Every piece of digital information we encounter is a result of coding improved through information theory.

When we hear about the information revolution that has taken shape around us, it is Shannon's 70-year-old concept that is still being invoked.

# CLASSICAL BITS

Games, from the simple Space Invaders (see below) to the more complex Fortnite, have evolved as information theory pushes the development of computer graphics. With the arrival of quantum computing, in which qubits replace classical bits, we can one day look forward to even greater processing power (see page 154). Although this change from transmitting data in bits – 1s and 0s – is not targeted at the entertainment industry, it is almost inevitable it will one day have a transformational impact on the games that future generations play.

# Can we make order from chaos theory?

**→ Chaos theory describes how the most complex systems in the world, which are governed by many predictable equations, ultimately end in chaos and disorder.**

Chaos theory, sometimes referred to as the 'butterfly effect', is a mathematical theory that underpins many behaviours seen in nature and everyday life.

In 1961, mathematician and meteorologist Edward Lorenz was trying to use computer models to predict changes in the weather. One evening, he ran his computer on two separate occasions, starting with slightly different numbers due to a rounding error. Lorenz expected the computer to predict weather outcomes that were also just slightly different, when in fact what he saw was deeply puzzling – the two scenarios predicted by the computer were completely different. This was the accidental birth of chaos theory.

Lorenz knew that weather relied upon many variables, such as wind speed, direction, humidity and temperature, among others. What he discovered was that as the system grew in complexity, small changes in the starting value of each initial condition propagated, leading to massive changes in the final outcome.

The formal name for this is deterministic chaos – sometimes referred to as a system being chaotic. Weather systems, for example, operate according to well-understood processes, which experts can model with mathematical equations. However, the sheer complexity of those systems means that the final outcome is actually often unpredictable.

Years later, Lorenz described his new theory to the world in a talk entitled 'Does the flap of a butterfly's wings in Brazil set off a tornado in Texas?'. Today, the theory helps to explain many phenomena seen in real life, such as unpredictable stock market behaviour, medical research trends, robotics and numerous scientific applications.

Although chaos theory sounds as if it should be about randomness, within it there are underlying patterns and repetition. For example, one of the most famous fields of study within chaos theory is fractals, a term coined by mathematician Benoit Mandelbrot. Mandelbrot showed that if you zoom in on certain objects, a seemingly endless level of detail is found, often in a repeating pattern. The mathematical beauty of fractals has since permeated into the arts, and they have been used as inspiration for films such as *Star Trek* and *Doctor Strange*.

# THE BUTTERFLY EFFECT

*Although not to be taken literally, the analogy of the flap of a butterfly's wings in Brazil causing a tornado in Texas highlights the key concept underpinning chaos theory. In highly complex systems, such as the Earth's climate, a tiny fluctuation in an initial condition (a butterfly flapping its wings) can have profound implications in other parts of the system sometime later.*

# Is life just a game theory?

**⟶ No. But the mathematics of game theory has proved to be a very useful tool to explain conflict and cooperation in fields as diverse as economics, evolutionary biology, political science and psychology.**

Over 100 years ago, mathematicians tried to forge a rigorous theory of competition. Chess master and mathematician Emanuel Lasker was among those who hoped that a new 'science of contest' would provide a rational means for resolving disputes, rendering war obsolete.

The first decisive step towards establishing modern game theory, however, was taken by the Hungarian-American genius John Von Neumann with his 1928 proof of the minimax theorem. The minimax theorem applies only to games with two opponents in which one person's loss is the other person's gain. Von Neumann coined the term zero-sum to describe such games of total conflict. He showed that for *every* two-player zero-sum game, from chess to rock-paper-scissors, there is a strategy for each player that guarantees the best outcome, assuming they are up against a rational player who is also exclusively out for themselves.

Von Neumann later tried to generalise the theory to include games with any number of players and in which the payoffs do not necessarily add up to zero. Written with the German economist Oskar Morgenstern and published in 1944, *Theory of Games and Economic Behavior* advanced a 'cooperative' game theory showing how players could sometimes team up against others to win – as is the case when a cartel colludes to raise prices for consumers.

But what if players could not, or simply did not want to, collaborate? In 1950, the American John Nash showed that in these circumstances, there are certain outcomes for all games (zero-sum or not, and with any number of participants), now called Nash equilibria, in which no player can do any better by unilaterally changing their strategy.

Nash's 'non-cooperative' game theory opened the floodgates in economics and elsewhere. Perhaps the most unexpected area of application was to animal behaviour, where game theory helped biologists to understand how cooperation might evolve in nature, famously 'red in tooth and claw'. Auctions designed by game theorists were used to sell off chunks of the radio spectrum to telecoms firms, making billions for governments. Today, game theorists make billions for technology titans by devising online advertising marketplaces, bidding systems and product-ranking algorithms.

# THE PRISONER'S DILEMMA

The most notorious 'game' to emerge from game theory is the 'prisoner's dilemma', describing a situation in which the most rational course of action for each side adds up to a worse outcome for everyone. Developed by defence analysts at the RAND Corporation in 1950, the game framed how some strategists viewed the nuclear standoff in the Cold War. The only Nash equilibrium is for the prisoners to confess to a crime they committed together – though if both prisoners talk, the outcome is worse than if they both do not.

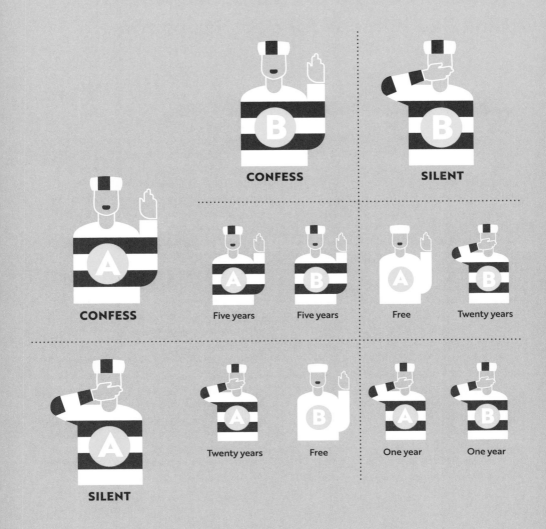

# Can machines learn to think like humans?

**⟶ Maybe one day, but not yet. We still don't fully understand how human brains work, so it's reasonable to assume that we won't be able to create machines that think like humans for decades to come.**

Artificial Intelligence (AI) – a term coined by American cognitive scientist John McCarthy in the 1950s – is a discipline that can generate lurid headlines. At its most dystopian, fears abound that if we create robots that think like us, they will annex the world.

The truth is that no computer has yet passed the Turing Test. Named after Alan Turing, the British mathematician and father of modern theoretical computer science, who died in 1954, it gauges a machine's ability to manifest intelligent behaviour that is indistinguishable from that of a human.

Today we have machines that translate Hindi into Māori, beat grandmasters at chess and identify anomalies in MRI scans before human doctors can – but still they don't think like humans do. They depend on machine learning, which requires vast amounts of data, far more than humans need, to learn something. What's more, each machine only gains specific skills, like playing a particular video game. This is not a route to flexible, human-like thinking, such as discussing the

sophistry of geopolitics or scrutinising the aesthetics of a Titian painting.

Creating a robot with human-like intelligence is fiendishly complex. Many AI experts consider it unfeasible, and it is questionable whether it is desirable. Nonetheless, there have been advances in programming based on neural networks – a subset of machine learning intended to simulate the way human brains operate. Neural networks use algorithms to recognise underlying patterns in data sets without having to follow comprehensive lists of instructions. To some extent their structure mimics the way biological neurons in human brains signal to each other.

Software using neural networks can be trained, through trial and error, to play board games or recognise faces, for example. Even so, this does not replicate human thought processes, which are conscious, autonomous and self-aware. One day, a machine with the ability to predict, desire, believe and so on – what philosophers call the 'theory of mind' – might be able to pass the Turing Test. Right now, that seems a long way off.

# THE TURING TEST

The Turing Test is conducted by an impartial judge. The test subjects – a real person and a computer – are hidden. The judge has a conversation with both parties and attempts to identify which is which, based on the quality of their conversation and their responses. If the judge can't tell the difference, the computer has succeeded in demonstrating human intelligence and has passed the test – it can think like a human.

# Who has claimed quantum supremacy?

→ **Google did so first, professing in 2019 to have demonstrated that its 54-qubit Sycamore quantum processor performed a calculation in 200 seconds that would have taken a classical computer centuries.**

Quantum supremacy is when a quantum computer can demonstrably solve a problem that no classical computer can solve in any reasonable amount of time. In 2019, Google claimed to have achieved this. Although rivals disputed the findings, others claimed it was a breakthrough equivalent to the Wright brothers' first flight.

Why is this a big deal? It all comes down to the complexity of quantum computers – devices that use the quantum states of subatomic particles to process information, instead of encoding information in binary 'bits' (see page 146) like a classical computer.

The basic unit of memory in a quantum computer is the qubit; these are created using subatomic particles such as electrons or photons. Qubits have quirky properties that mean a connected group of them can provide far more processing power than classical binary bits. For example, unlike a normal computer bit, a qubit can be a 0 or a 1, but crucially also a superposition of both at the same time. Entanglement is another vital, complex property of qubits, which Albert Einstein once described as 'spooky action at a distance'.

These properties are what give quantum computers their advantage in situations where there are large numbers of possible combinations – for example, when trying to predict the future movements of financial markets. Quantum computers can consider all the possibilities simultaneously, whereas classical computers would have to consider each in turn. Finding a needle in a haystack is easier with a quantum computer.

The power of a quantum computer grows exponentially with more qubits. A thousand entangled qubits represent more numbers than there are atoms in the universe.

It will still be some time before the practical applications of quantum computers become truly apparent. Meanwhile, the quantum state of qubits means they are extremely fragile, making them error prone and liable to 'crash' in a process known as quantum decoherence. As a result, they require protective environments such as vacuums and extremely cold operating temperatures. This means that for most everyday situations, classical computers will still hold sway for a long time.

# QUANTUM COMPUTING

*A classical computer bit can have two states – a 0 or a 1 – and information is transmitted in either of these two forms. A qubit can be a 1, a 0, or a 'superposition' of both – the maths around this is complicated – but it means the computer's ability to process information increases exponentially. The term 'quantum supremacy' was coined by theoretical physicist John Preskill in 2012. Google's claim of quantum supremacy, and similar assertions by Chinese researchers, led to lurid headlines insisting no code – from your banking password to nuclear weapons systems – was now unbreakable. But the truth is that quantum computing has a way to go before it will usurp classical information technology.*

**QUANTUM COMPUTER**

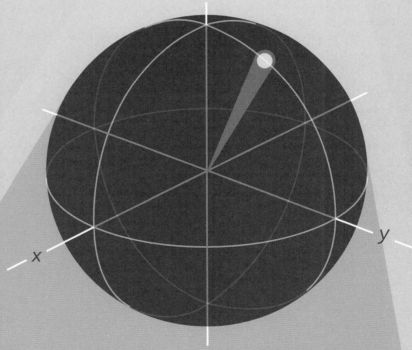

The Bloch sphere represents all the possible states for a single qubit.

**CLASSICAL COMPUTER**

0 ——————— 1

# FURTHER EXPLORATION

Arney, Kat. *How to Code a Human*. London: Welbeck Publishing, 2017

Asimov, I. *Biographical Encyclopedia of Science and Technology*. New York: Doubleday. Revised, subsequent edition, 1982

Bhattacharya, Ananyo. *The Man from the Future: The Visionary Life of John von Neumann*. London: Allen Lane, 2021

Bodanis, D. *E=mc²: A Biography of the World's Most Famous Equation*. London: Pan MacMillan, 2016

Chalmers, A. F. *What Is This Thing Called Science?* Cambridge, MA: Hackett Publishing Company; 4th edition, 2013

Clegg, Brian. *Ten Patterns That Explain the Universe*. Cambridge, MA: MIT Press, 2021

Close, F, Marten M. and Sutton C. *The Particle Explosion*. Oxford: Oxford University Press, 1986

Gleick, James. *Chaos*. New York: Viking, 1987

Meadows, D. H. et al. 'The Limits to Growth'. A Report for the Club of Rome's Project on the Predicament of Mankind, 1972

Pilcher, Helen. *Life Changing – How Humans are Altering Life on Earth*. London: Bloomsbury Sigma, 2020

Pilcher, Helen. *Mind Maps Biology: How to Navigate the Living World*. Cheltenham: The History Press, 2020

Pratt, Carl J. *Quantum Physics for Beginners: From Wave Theory to Quantum Computing. Understanding How Everything Works by a Simplified Explanation of Quantum Physics and Mechanics*. Stefano Solimito, 2021

Rae, Alastair I. M. *Quantum Mechanics*. Cambridge: Cambridge University Press, 2012

Still, Ben. *Mind Maps Physics: How to Navigate the World of Science*. Cheltenham: The History Press, 2020

Strathern, P. *Mendeleyev's Dream: The Quest for the Elements*. London: Pegasus Books, 2019

Wooster, Jeremy. *Quantum Physics For Beginners: The Simple Guide to Discovering How Theories of Quantum Physics Can Change Your Everyday Life. The Secrets of New Scientific Knowledge Made Uncomplicated and Practical*. USA: Independently published, 2022

## ONLINE RESOURCES

*Chemistry World*
www.chemistryworld.com

*Nature*
www.nature.com

*New Scientist*
www.newscientist.com

*Science Focus*
www.sciencefocus.com

# NOTES ON CONTRIBUTORS

## CONSULTANT EDITOR

### Mark Peplow

Mark Peplow is a science writer with 20 years of experience as a reporter and editor. He was formerly chief news editor at *Nature* and editor of *Chemistry World*. His writing spans the physical sciences: from astrophysics and planetary sciences, through chemistry and materials, to Earth and environmental science.

Mark has a Masters in chemistry from the University of Oxford, a PhD in organometallic chemistry from Imperial College London, and an MSc in Science Communication from Imperial. He lives in Penrith, UK, and spends as much time as possible hiking the Lake District fells.

## ILLUSTRATOR

### Robert Brandt

Based in the UK, for over twenty years Robert Brandt has been a visual communicator with a focus on illustrating technical and scientific subjects ranging from astrophysics to biochemistry. He works with experts to make complex topics accessible to a wide audience in publishing, industry and education.

## CONTRIBUTORS

### Ananyo Bhattacharya

Ananyo Bhattacharya holds a degree in physics from the University of Oxford and a PhD in protein crystallography from Imperial College London. He is a science writer who has worked at *The Economist* and *Nature*.

### Thomas Buggey

Thomas Buggey is a post-doctoral researcher at the Centre for Electronic Imaging at the Open University, with a broad background in physics, astronomy and space science instrumentation. His current areas of research include development of detectors on space telescopes for large space agencies such as NASA and ESA.

### Mick O'Hare

Mick O'Hare specialises in writing about science and space history. A former editor at *New Scientist* he now writes for *The Independent* and *The New European* among others.

### Helen Pilcher

Helen Pilcher has a PhD in cell biology from London's Institute of Psychiatry, as well as degrees in psychology and neuroscience. She used to work as a reporter for *Nature*, and managed the Royal Society's Science in Society Program. She now writes and talks about science. She has penned many popular science books, as well as news and features for the likes of *The Guardian*, *New Scientist* and *Science Focus*.

### Sheona Urquhart

Sheona Urquhart is a researcher and lecturer in astrophysics at the Open University. Her current areas of research and interest include the large scale structures of the universe and high redshift galaxies.

# INDEX

# ACKNOWLEDGEMENTS

I'd like to thank our indefatigable
commissioning editor Kate Duffy for all
her guidance in creating this book, and our
copy editor Karen Packham for her patience
and painstaking attention to detail. I'm
grateful to all of the book's co-authors for
their insights into scientific fields far beyond
my ken. Big hugs to my daughters Maia and
Emily, who have been enthusiastic sounding
boards for so many of the ideas in this book.
Most of all, thanks to my wife Lianne, who
makes it all possible.

Mark Peplow